EASY PIANO EDITION

GREAT PIANO SOLOS

Published by
Wise Publications
14-15 Berners Street, London W1T 3LJ, UK.

Exclusive Distributors:
Music Sales Limited
Distribution Centre, Newmarket Road, Bury St Edmunds, Suffolk IP33 3YB, UK.
Music Sales Pty Limited
20 Resolution Drive, Caringbah, NSW 2229, Australia.

Order No. AM993542
ISBN: 978-1-84772-545-5
This book © Copyright 2008 Wise Publications,
a division of Music Sales Limited.

Edited by Jenni Wheeler.
Arranged and engraved by Camden Music.

Cover image based on original sculpture,
The Horn of Africa, 2006 by Michael Parekowhai
Courtesy of the artist and Roslyn Oxley9 Gallery
Cover designed by Liz Barrand.

Printed in the EU.

EASY PIANO EDITION

GREAT PIANO SOLOS

WISE PUBLICATIONS
part of The Music Sales Group
London / New York / Paris / Sydney / Copenhagen / Berlin / Madrid / Tokyo

CLASSICAL MUSIC

FILM THEMES

GREAT STANDARDS

Air On The G String

Composed by Johann Sebastian Bach

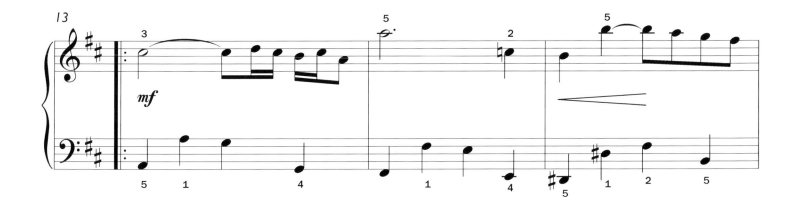

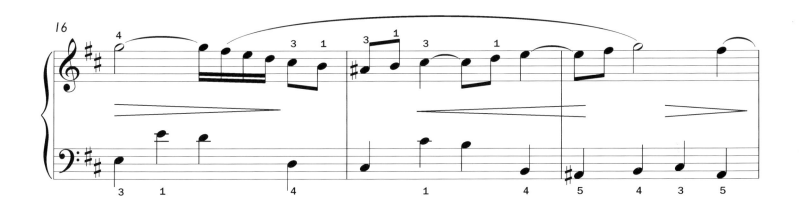

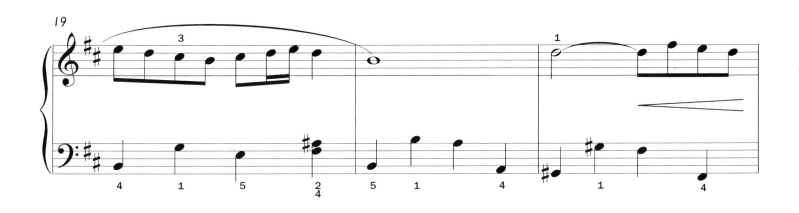

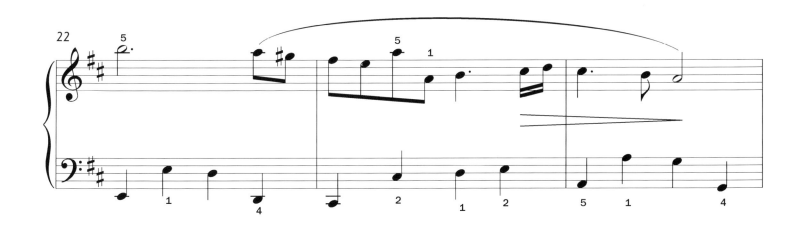

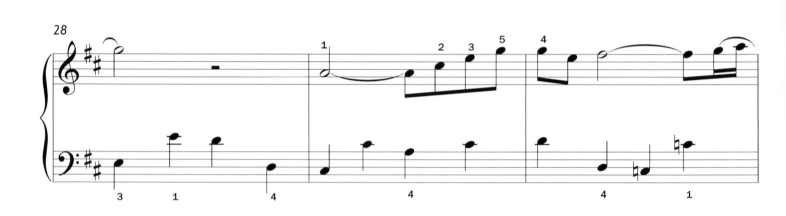

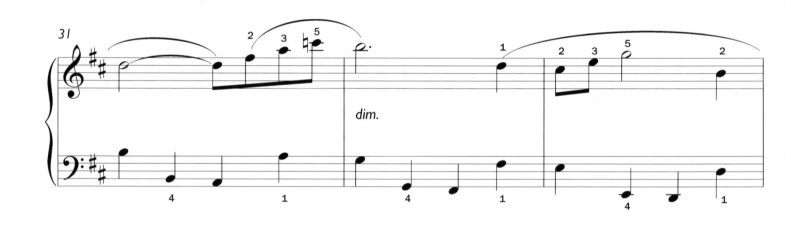

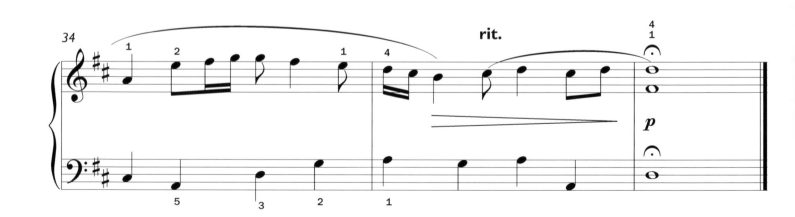

Pie Jesu

(from 'Requiem, Op. 48')

Composed by Gabriel Fauré

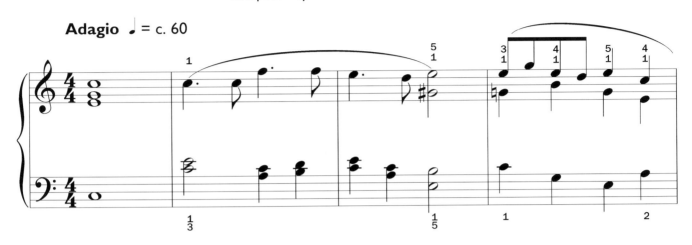

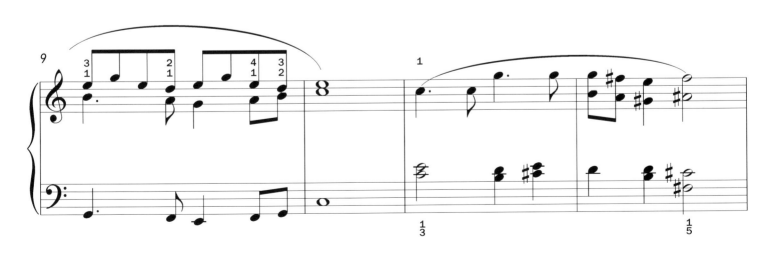

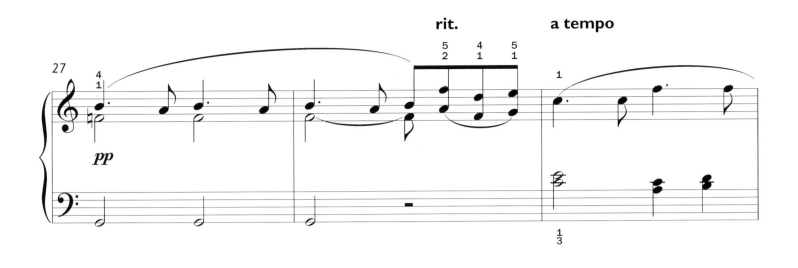
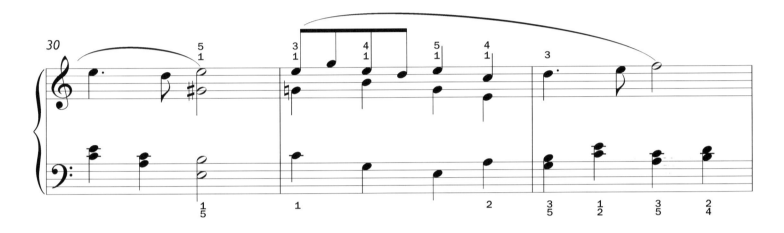

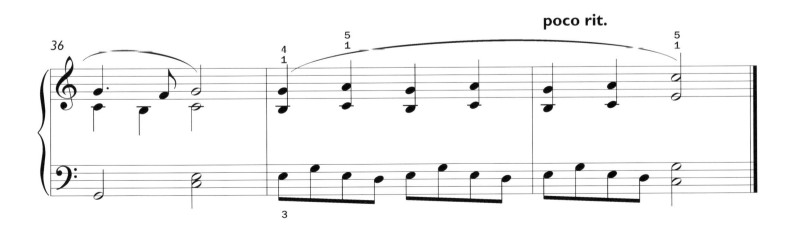

Liebestraume: Notturno No. 3

Composed by Franz Liszt

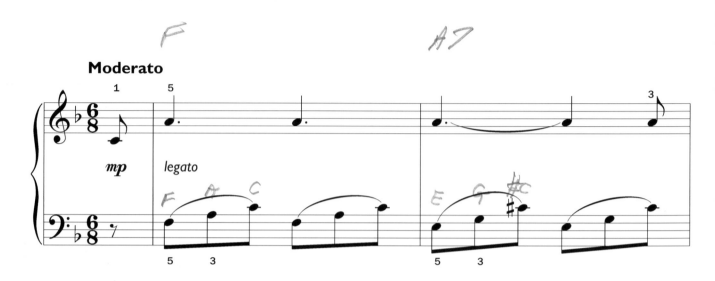

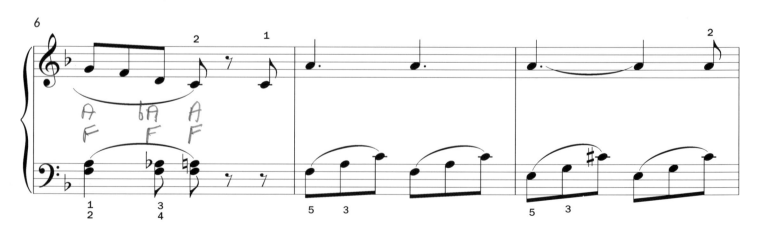

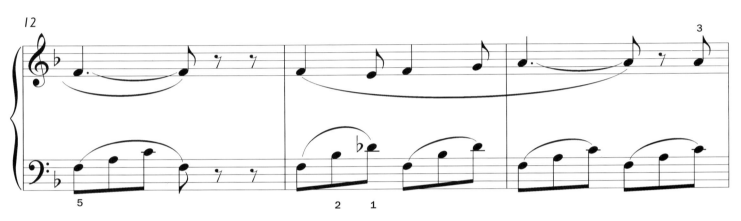

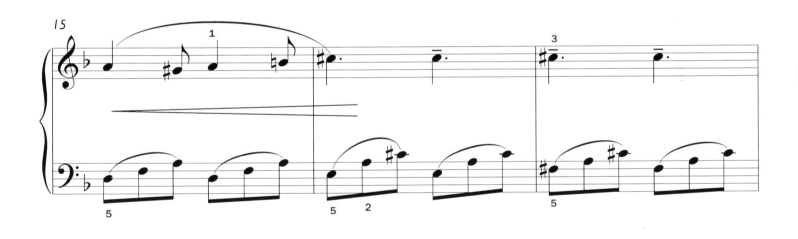

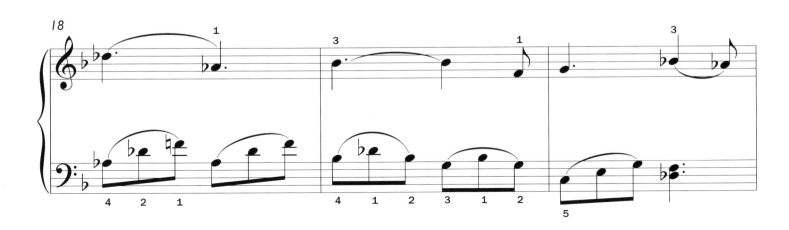

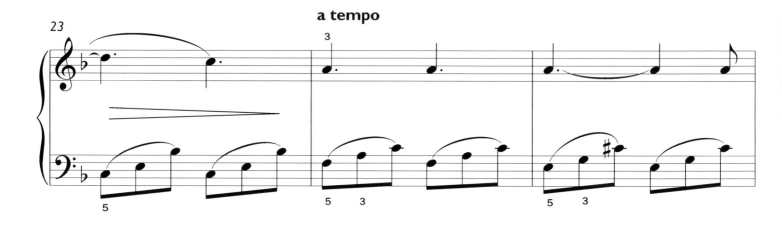

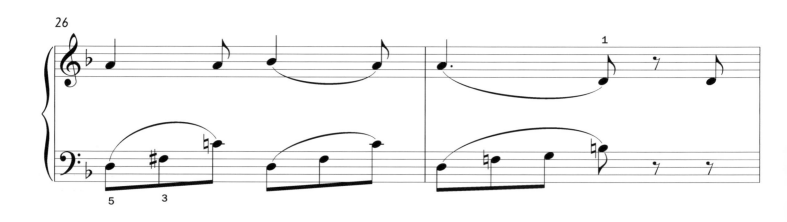

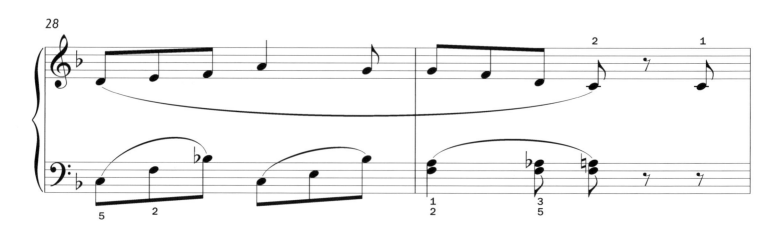

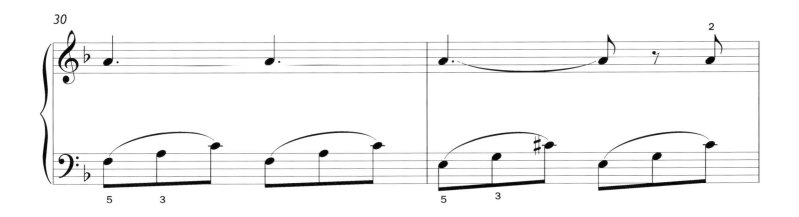

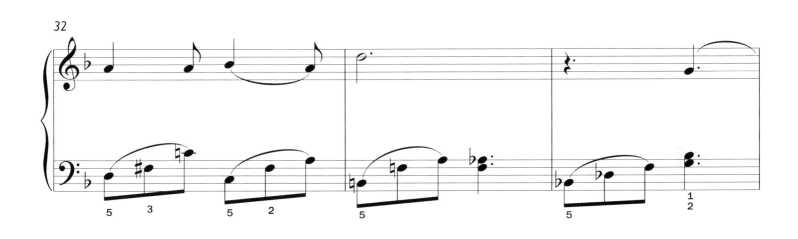

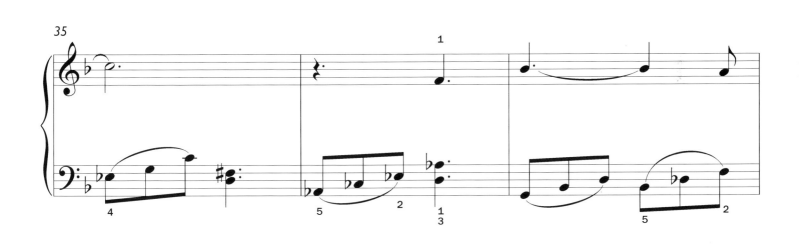

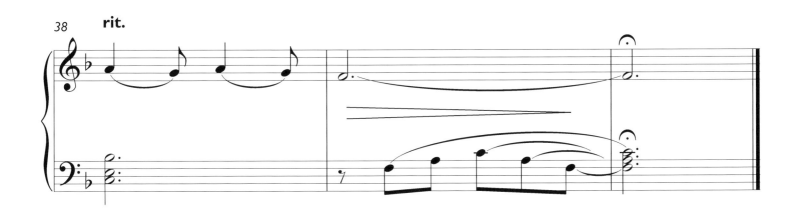

Ode To Joy

(from 'Symphony No. 9', 4th Movement)

Composed by Ludwig Van Beethoven

Allegro ♩ = 120

Piano Sonata In C, K545

(Allegro)

Composed by Wolfgang Amadeus Mozart

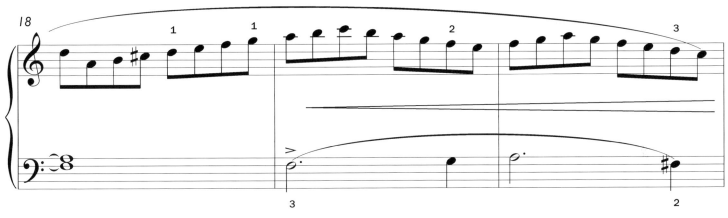

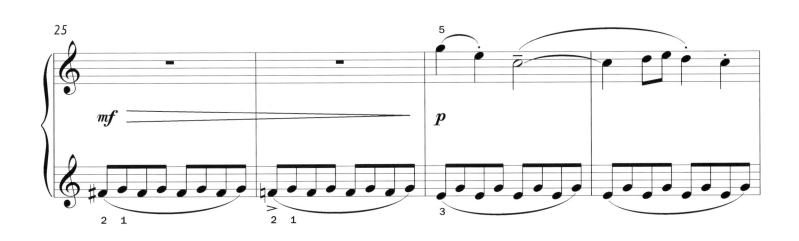

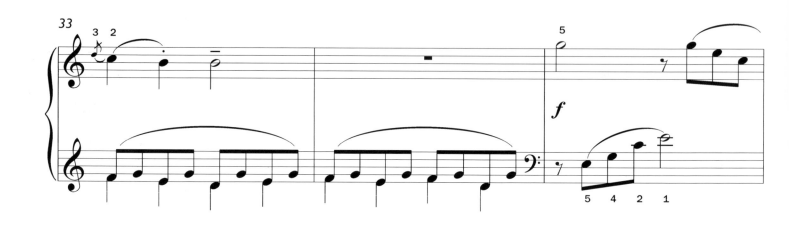

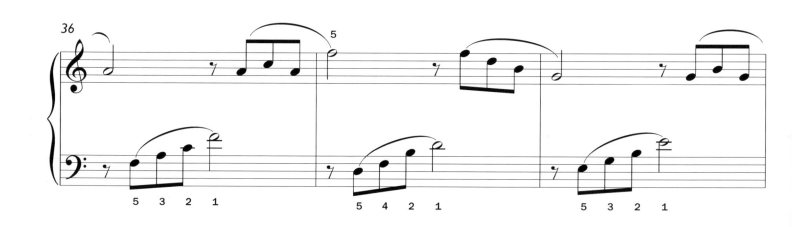

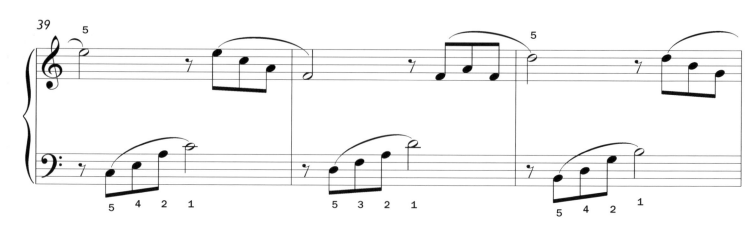

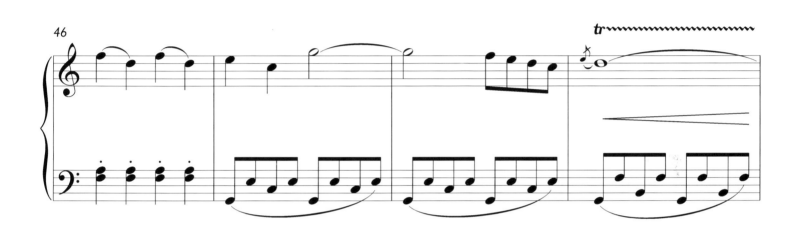

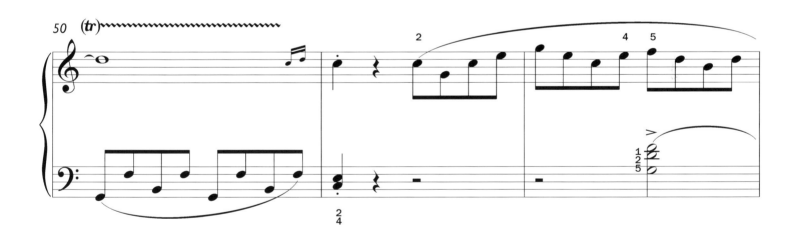

Born Free

Words by Don Black, Music by John Barry

-rounds you, the world still a - stounds you each

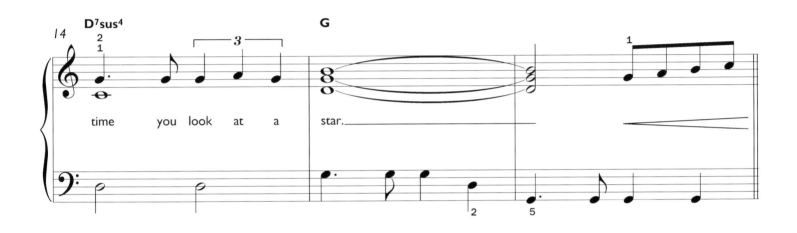

time you look at a star.

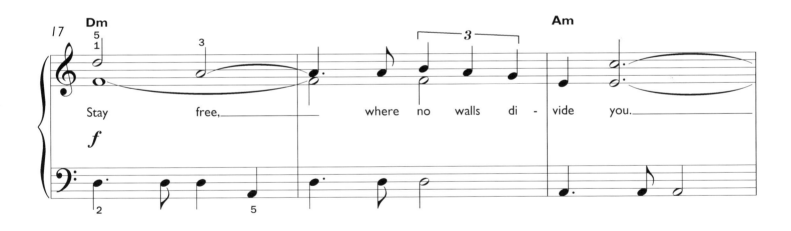

Stay free, where no walls di - vide you.

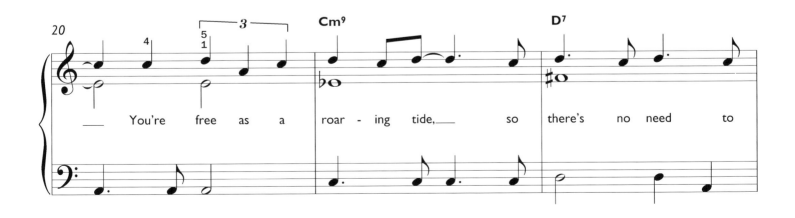

You're free as a roar - ing tide, so there's no need to

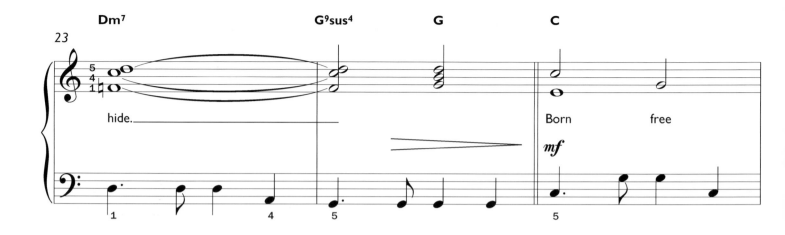

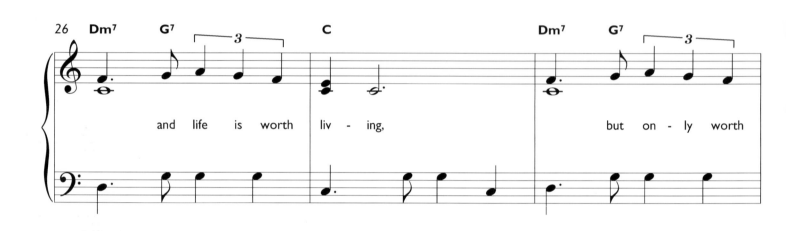

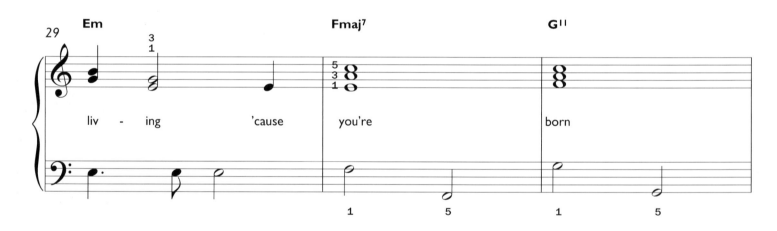

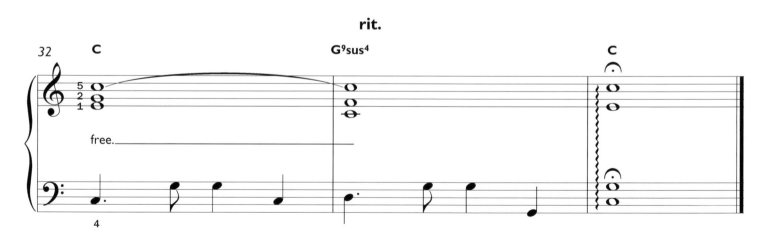

Mission: Impossible

Music by Lalo Schifrin

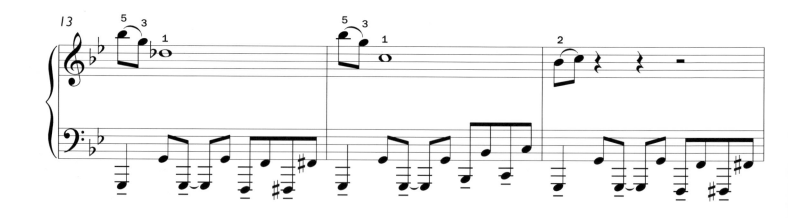

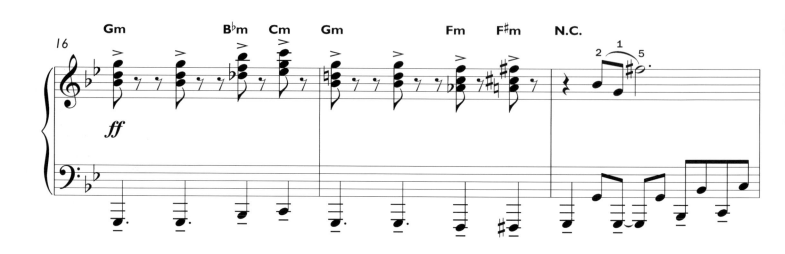

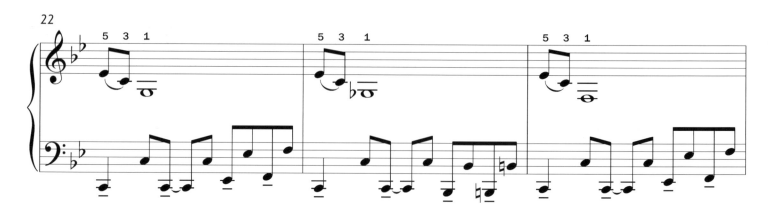

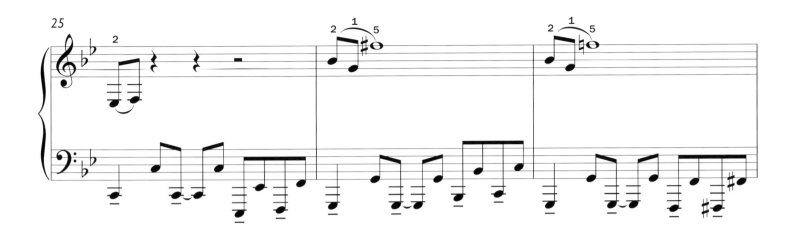

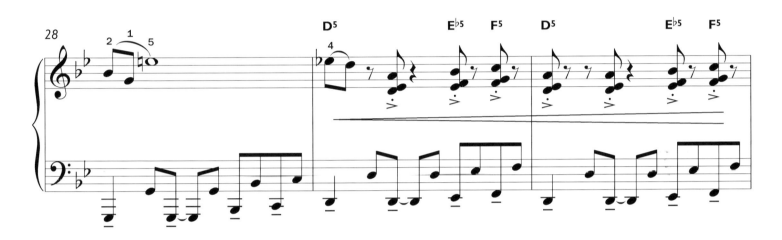

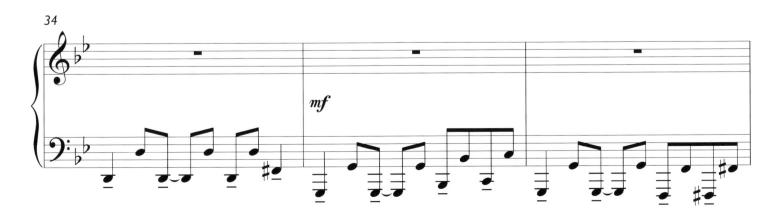

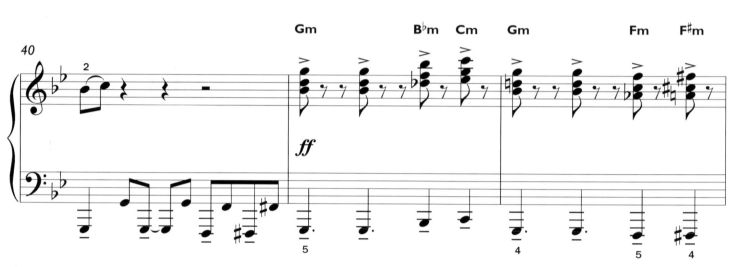

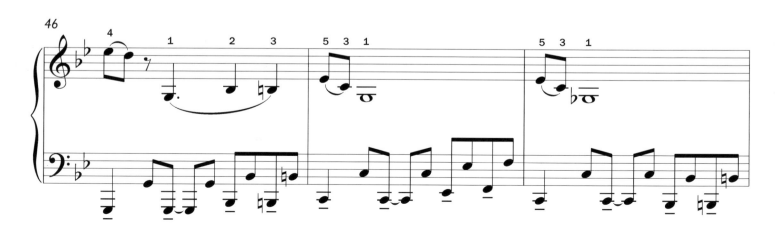

play 3 times

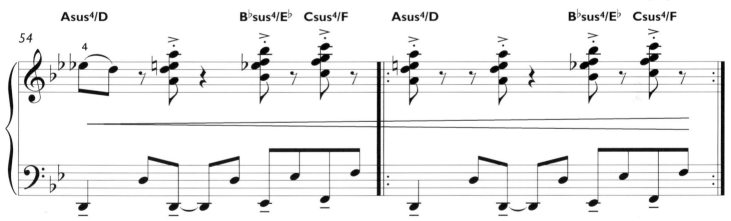

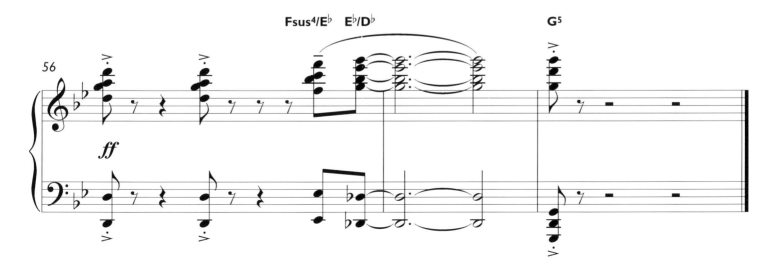

The Godfather

(Love Theme)

Music by Nino Rota

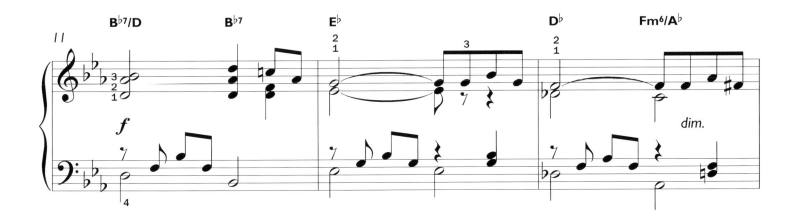

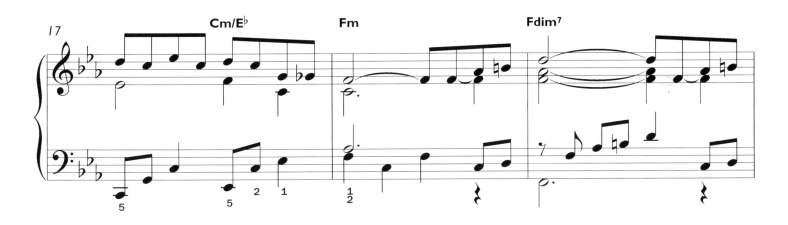

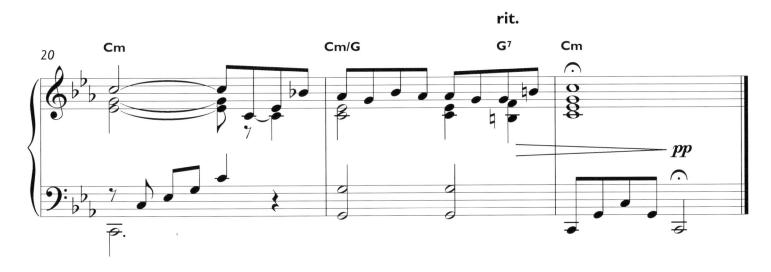

Jurassic Park

Music by John Williams

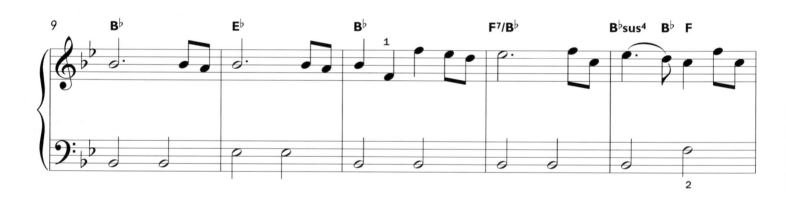

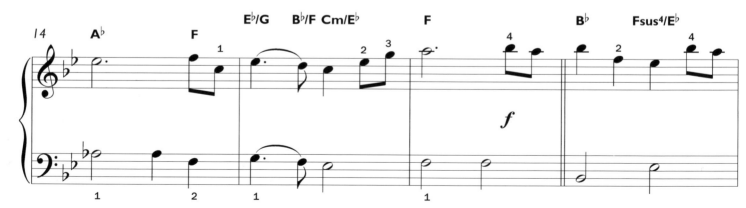

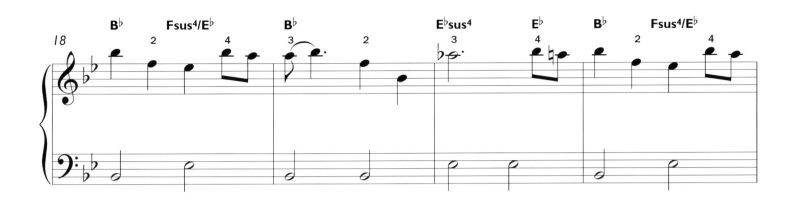

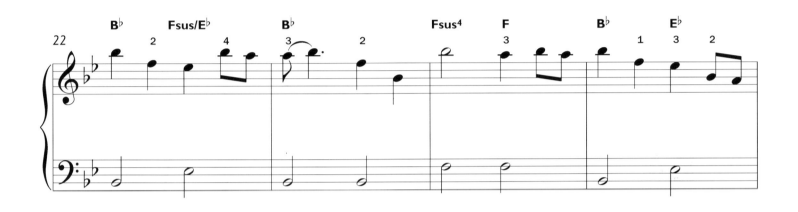

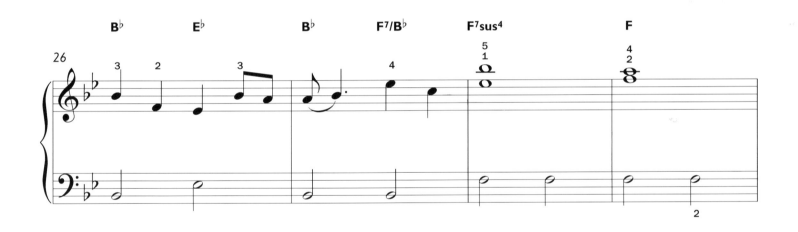

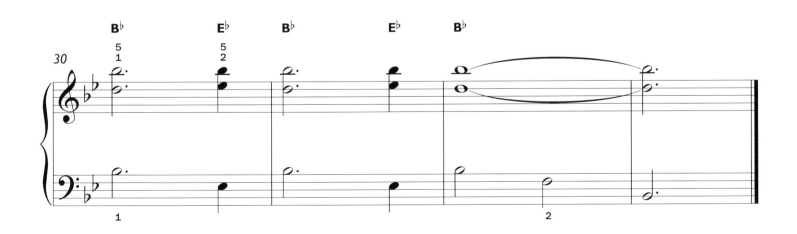

Where Do I Begin

(Theme from 'Love Story')

Words by Carl Sigman, Music by Francis Lai

Can't Help Falling In Love

Words & Music by George David Weiss, Hugo Peretti & Luigi Creatore

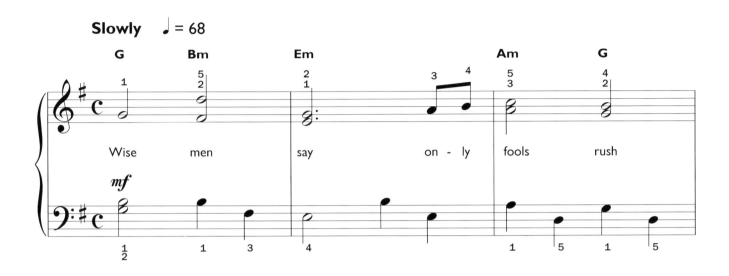

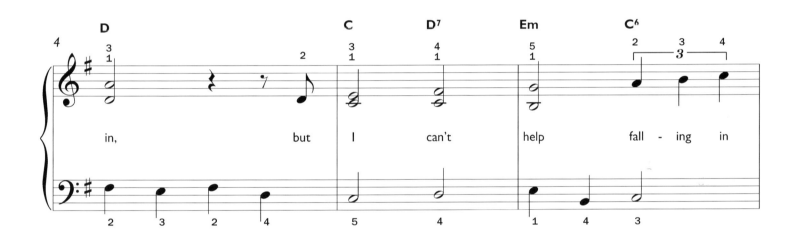

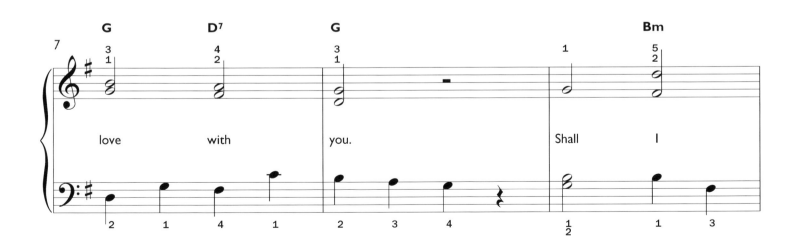

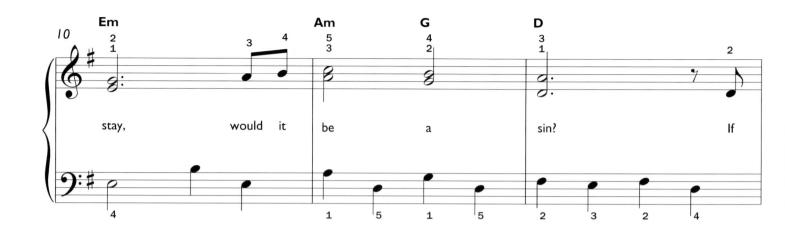

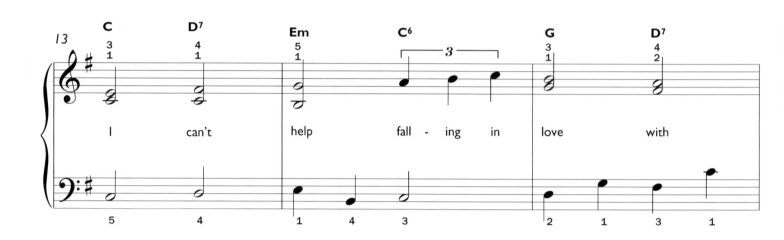

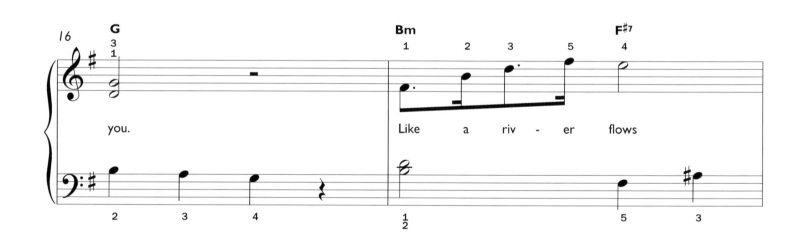

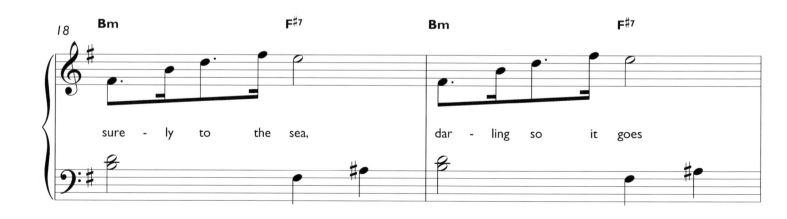

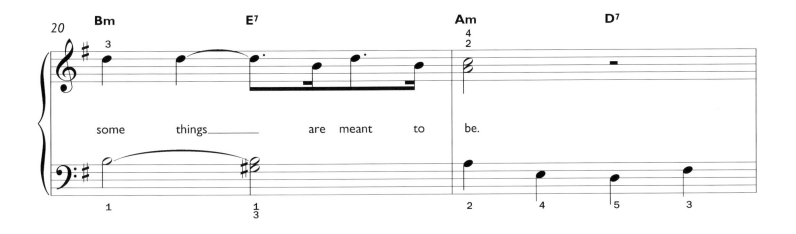

some things_____ are meant to be.

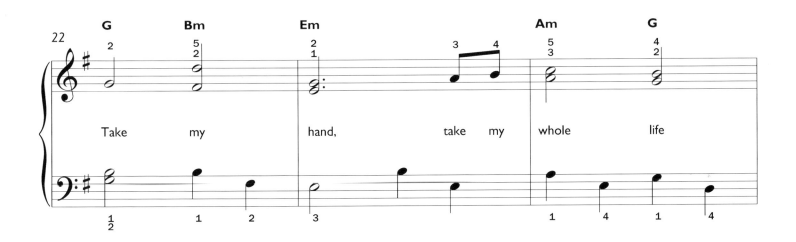

Take my hand, take my whole life

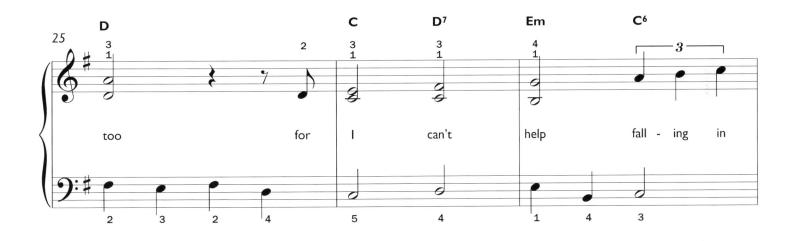

too for I can't help fall - ing in

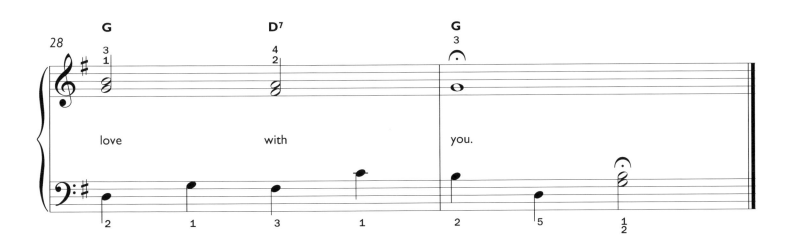

love with you.

Smoke Gets In Your Eyes

Words by Otto Harbach, Music by Jerome Kern

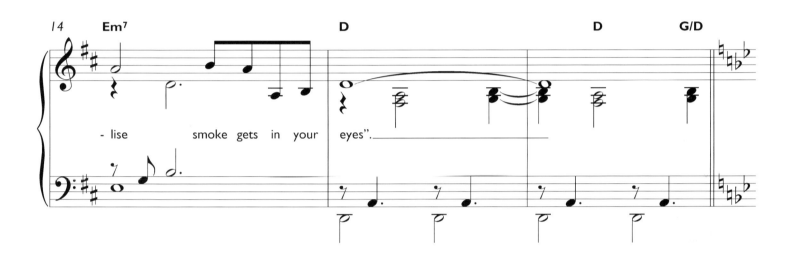

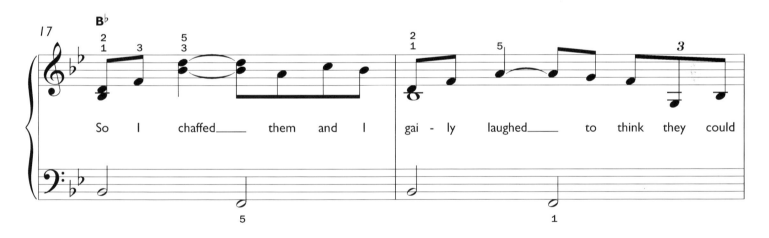

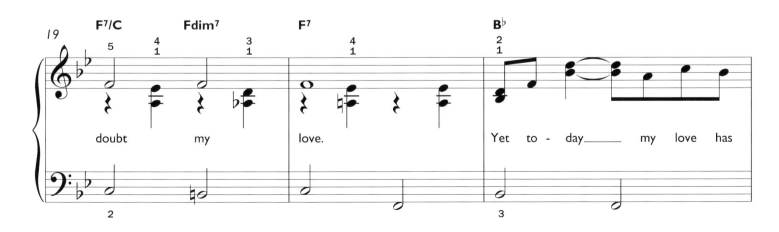

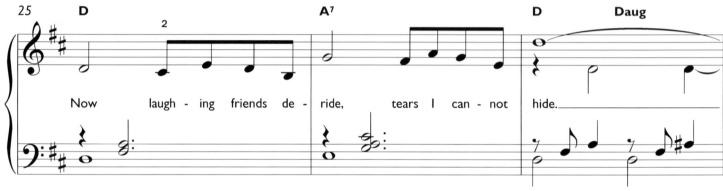

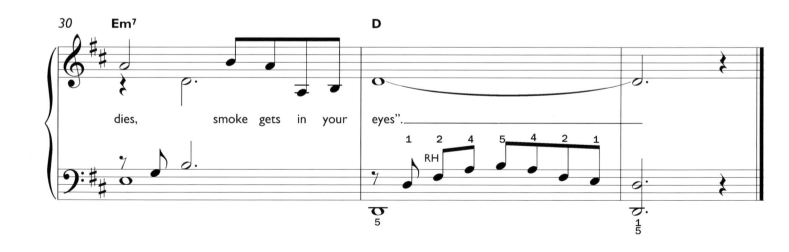

These Foolish Things

Words by Eric Maschwitz, Music by Jack Strachey

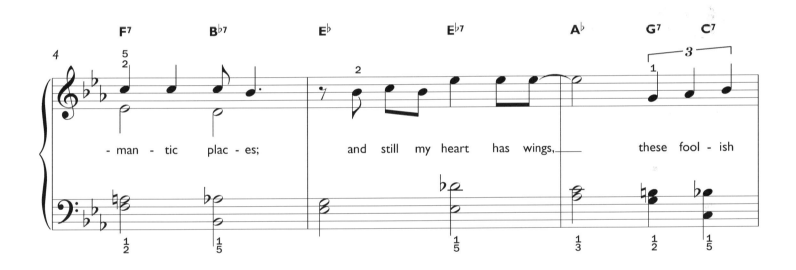

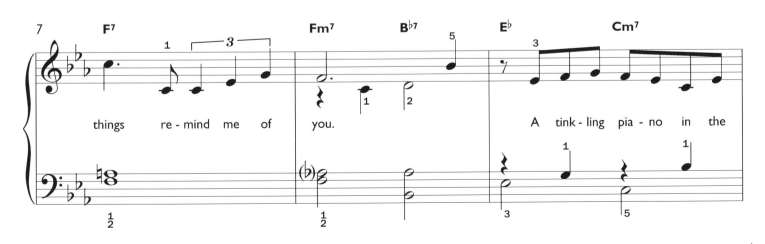

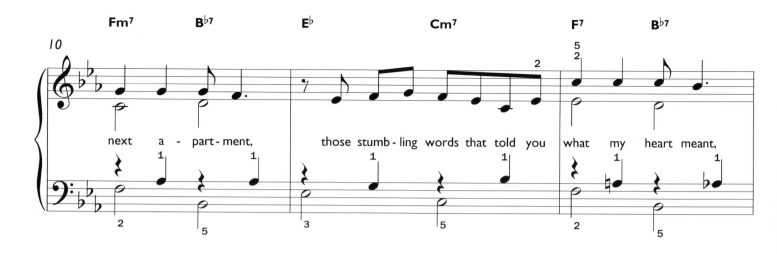

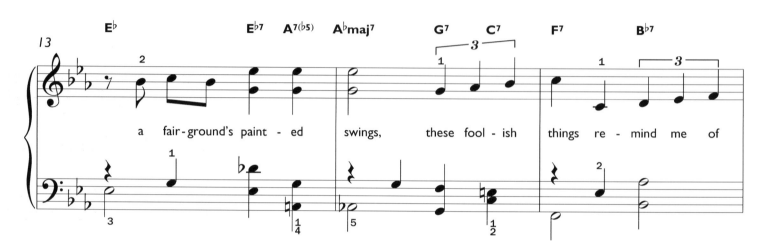

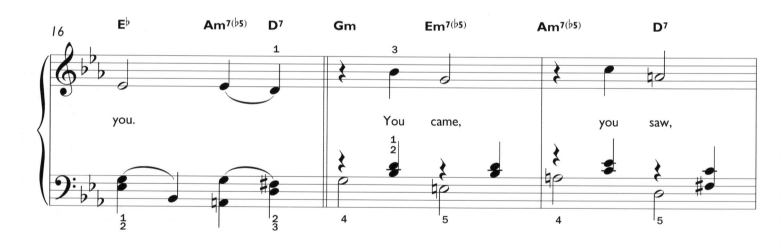

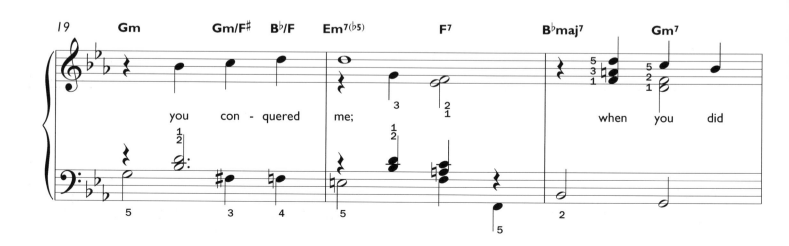

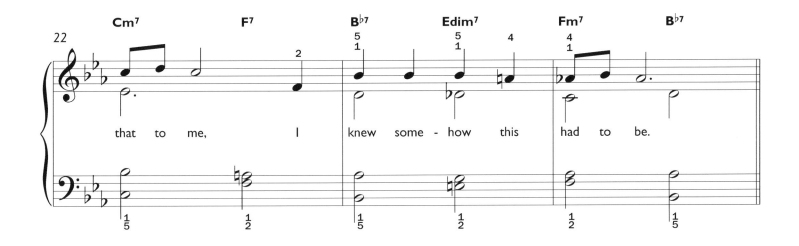

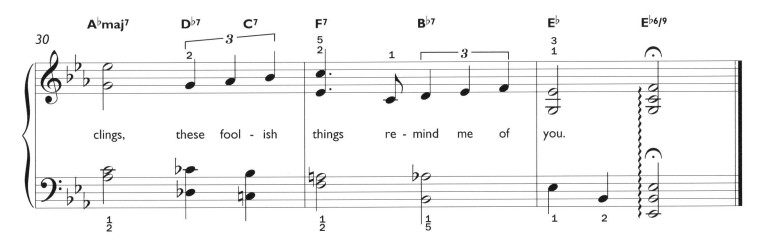

Unchained Melody

Words by Hy Zaret, Music by Alex North

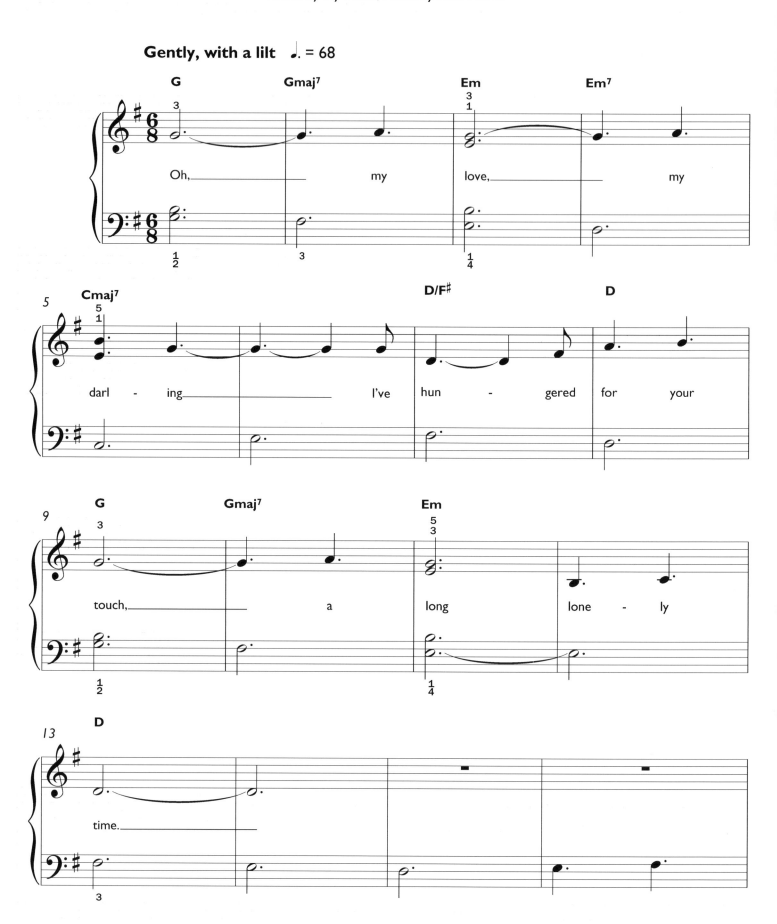

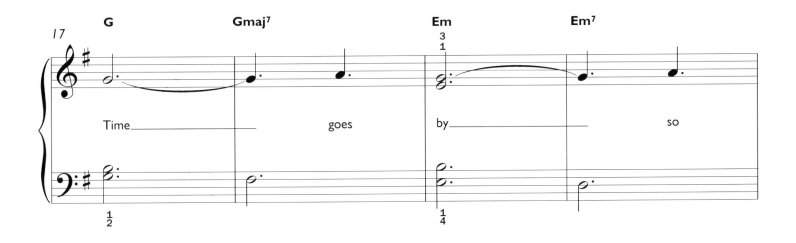

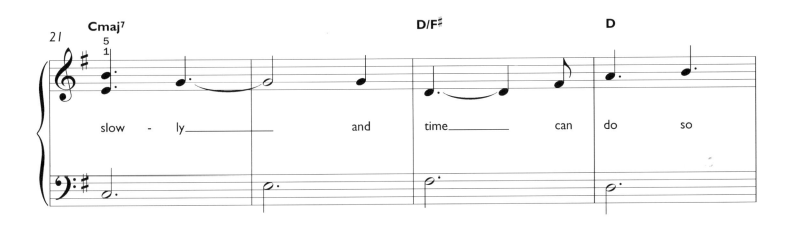

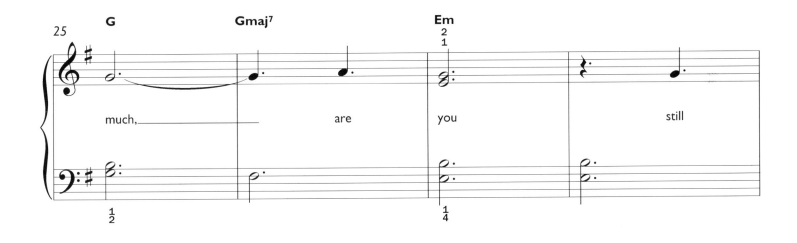

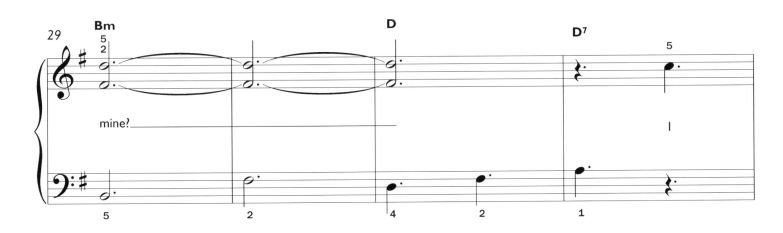

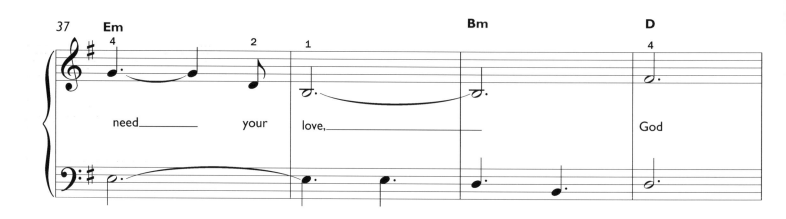

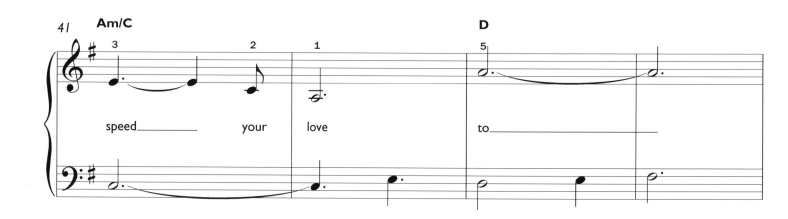

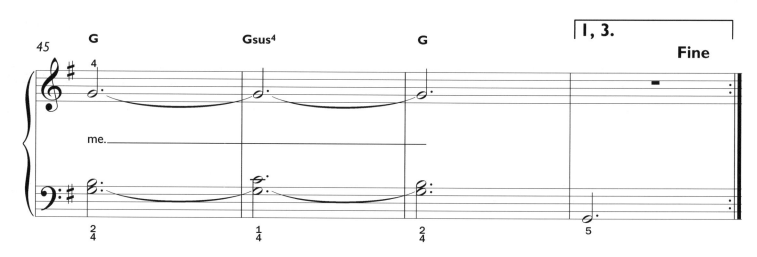

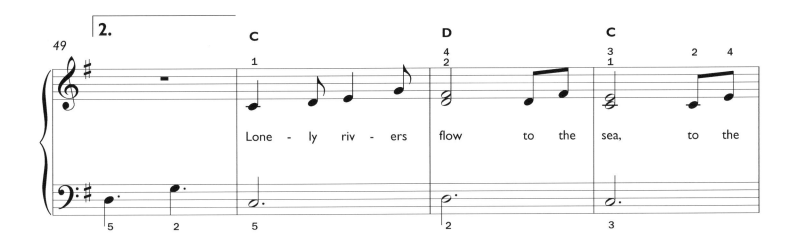

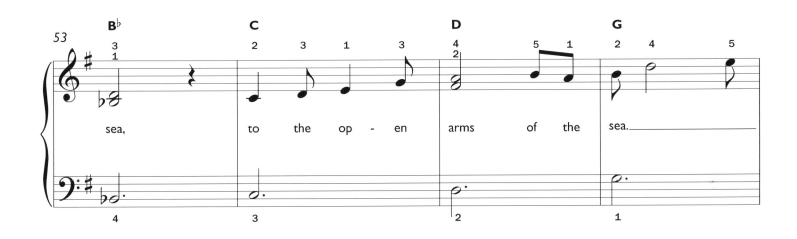

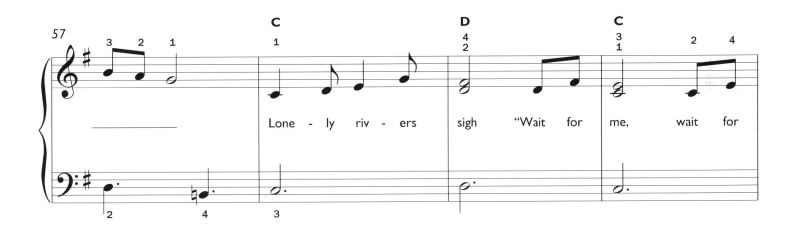

D.C. al Fine

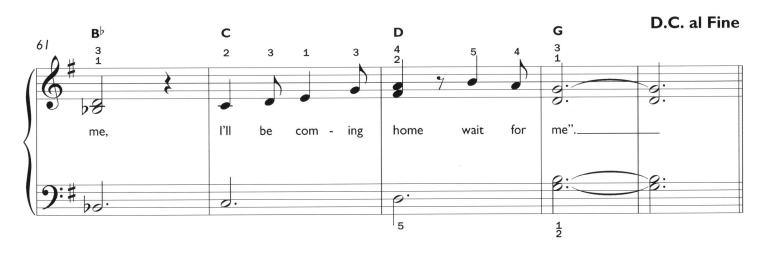

The Way You Look Tonight

Words by Dorothy Fields, Music by Jerome Kern

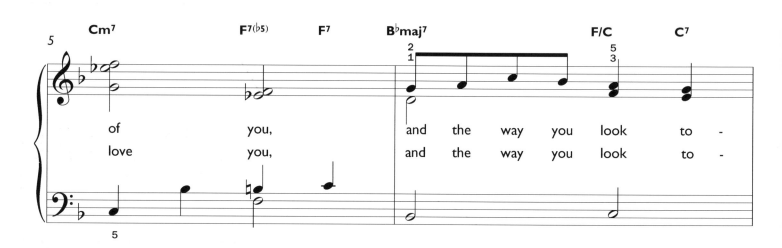

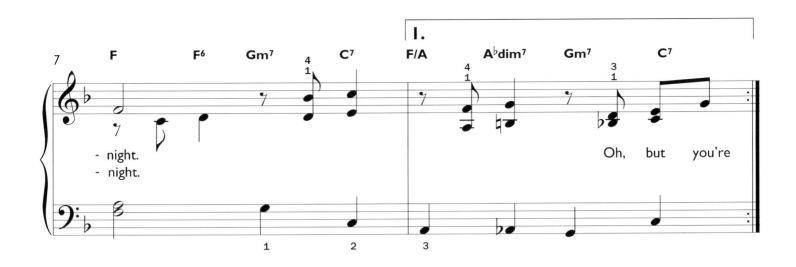

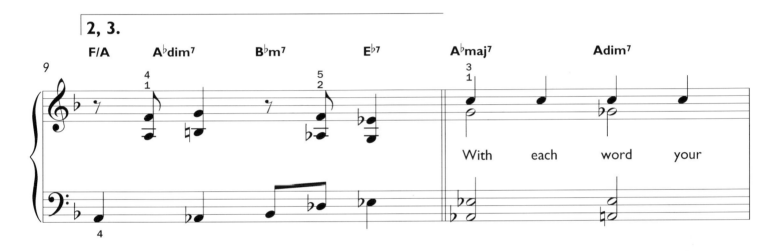

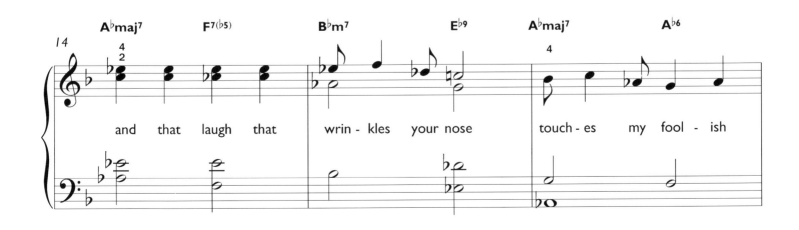

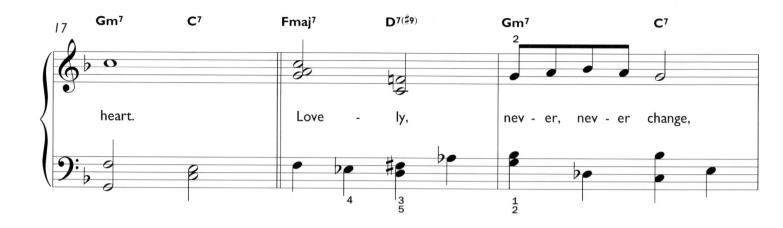

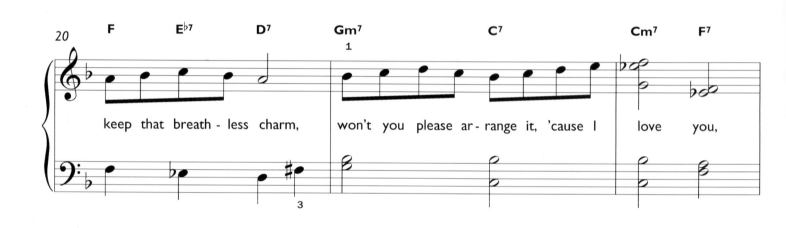

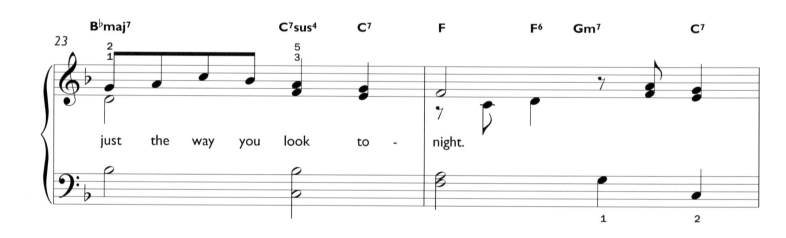

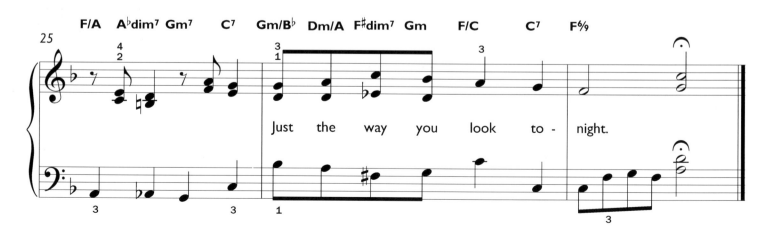

In A Sentimental Mood

Words & Music by Duke Ellington, Irving Mills & Manny Kurtz

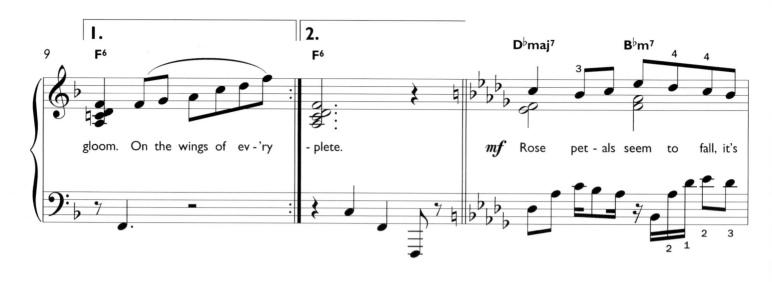

gloom. On the wings of ev-'ry - plete. *mf* Rose pet-als seem to fall, it's

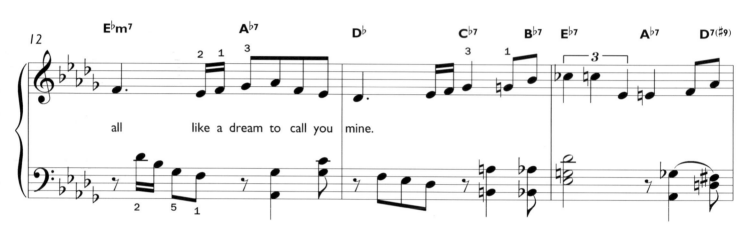

all like a dream to call you mine.

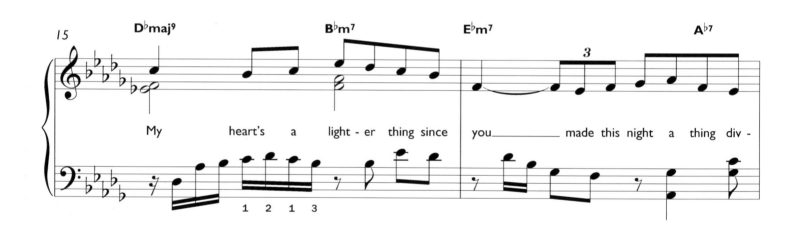

My heart's a light-er thing since you____ made this night a thing div-

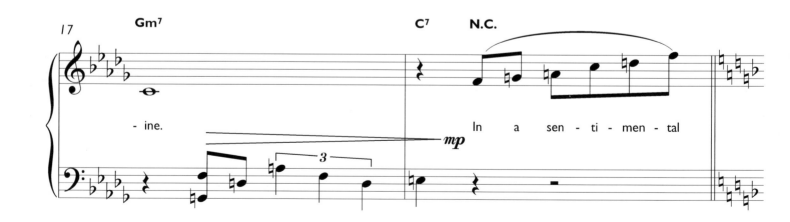

- ine. *mp* In a sen-ti-men-tal

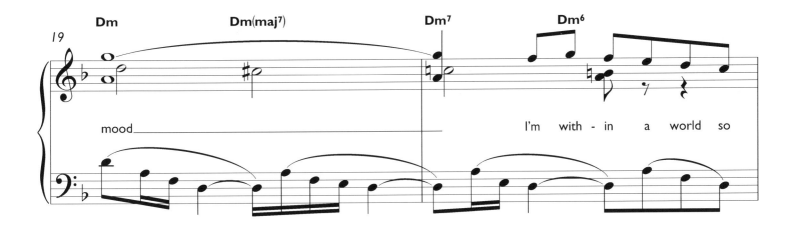

mood _____ I'm with - in a world so

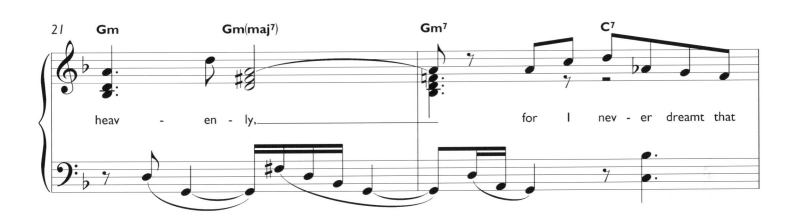

heav - en - ly, _____ for I nev - er dreamt that

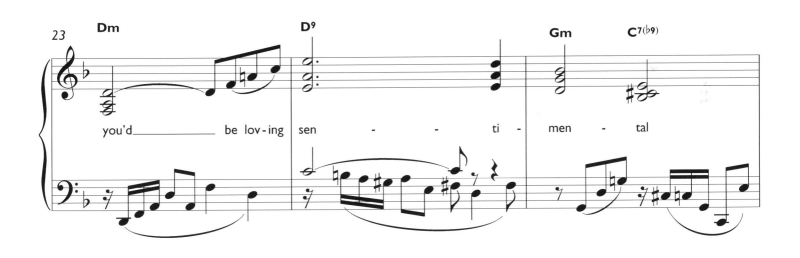

you'd _____ be lov-ing sen - - ti - men - tal

me.

pp

Honeysuckle Rose

Words by Andy Razaf, Music by Fats Waller

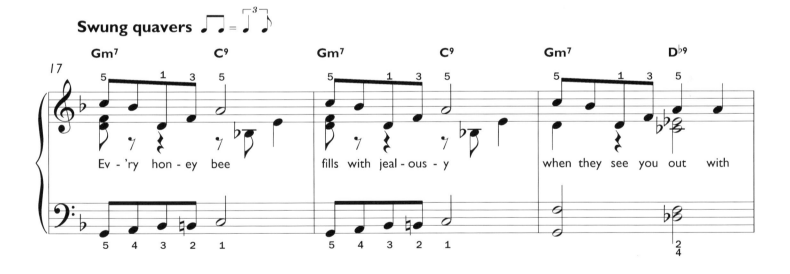

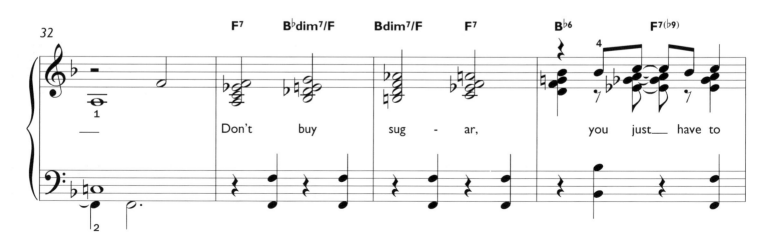

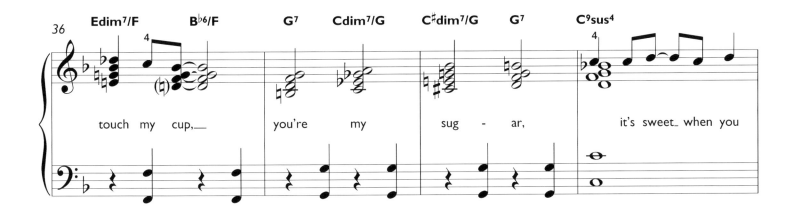

touch my cup,___ you're my sug - ar, it's sweet_ when you

stir it up.___ When I'm tak - in' sips from your tast - y lips,

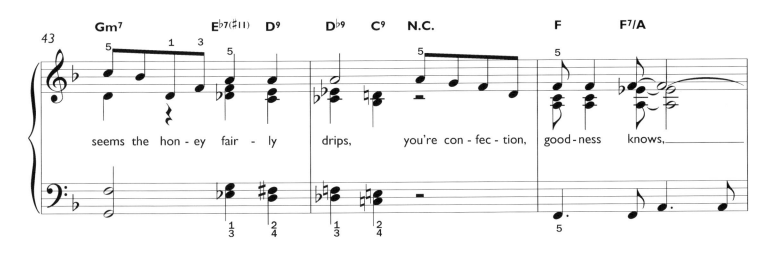

seems the hon - ey fair - ly drips, you're con - fec - tion, good - ness knows,___

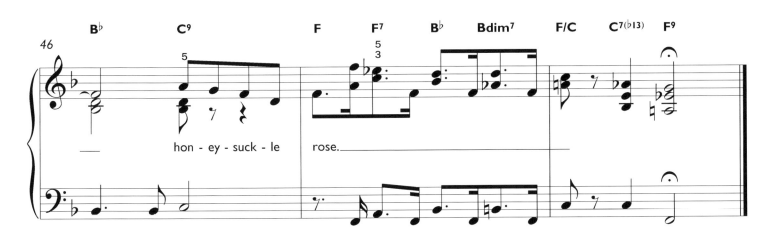

___ hon - ey - suck - le rose.___

The Lady Sings The Blues

Words by Billie Holiday, Music by Herbie Nichols

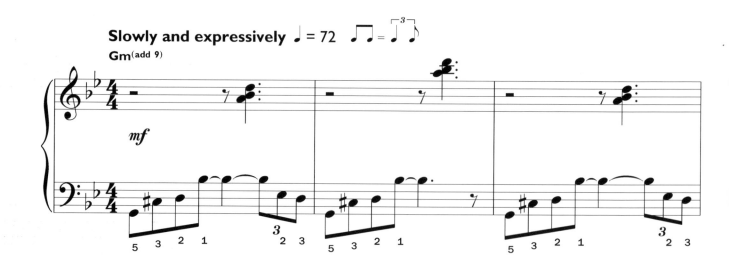

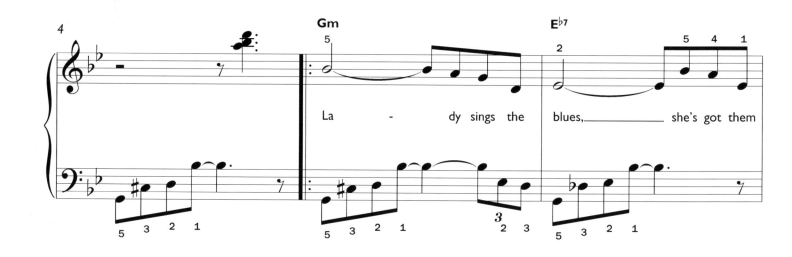

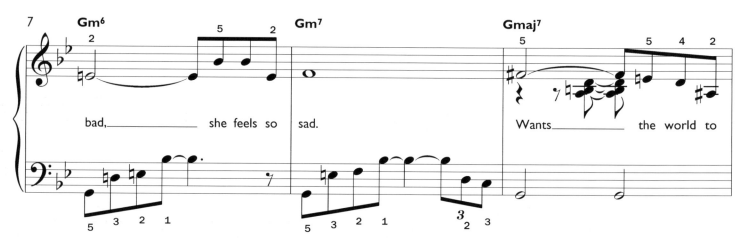

know___ just what the blues is all a-bout.___

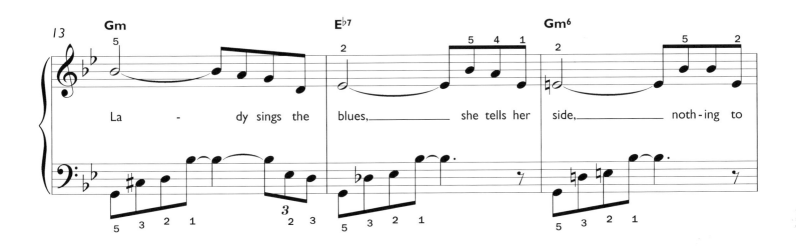

La - dy sings the blues,___ she tells her side,___ noth-ing to

hide. Now___ the world will know___ just what the

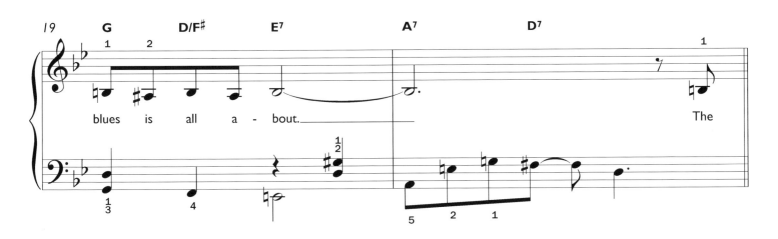

blues is all a-bout.___ The

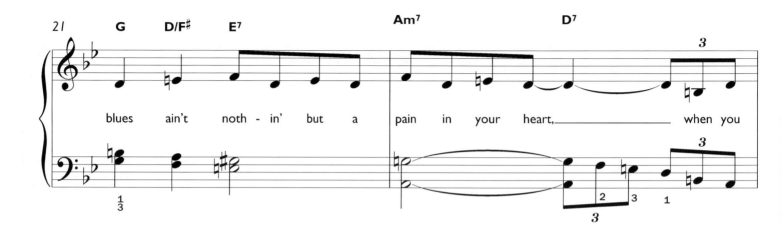

blues ain't noth-in' but a pain in your heart,_____ when you

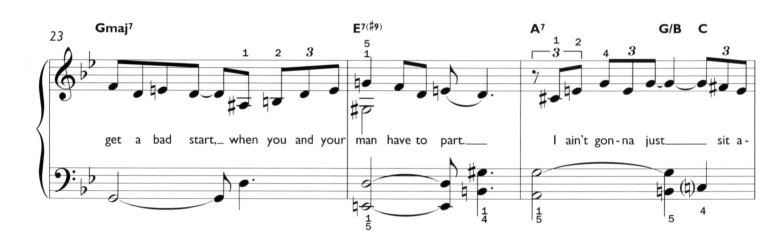

get a bad start,__ when you and your man have to part.__ I ain't gon-na just_____ sit a-

-round____ and cry,____ and now I know I won't die,____ be-cause I

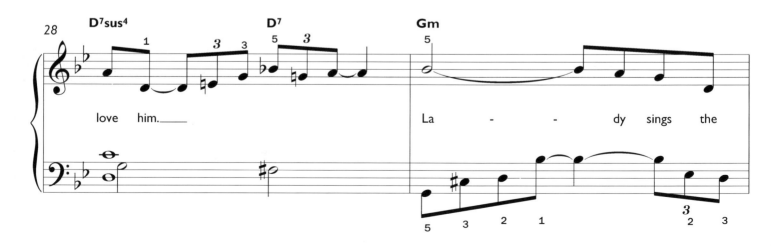

love him.____ La — — dy sings the

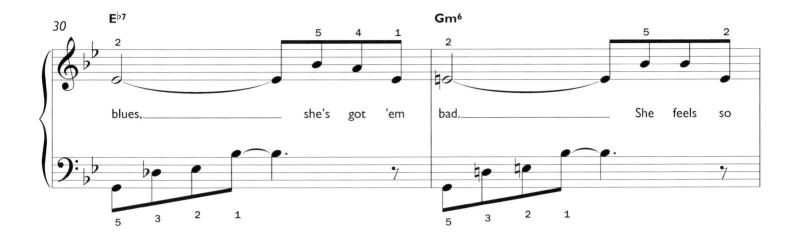

blues,_____ she's got 'em bad._____ She feels so

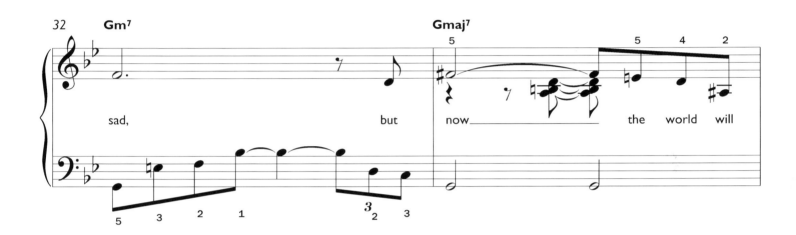

sad, but now_____ the world will

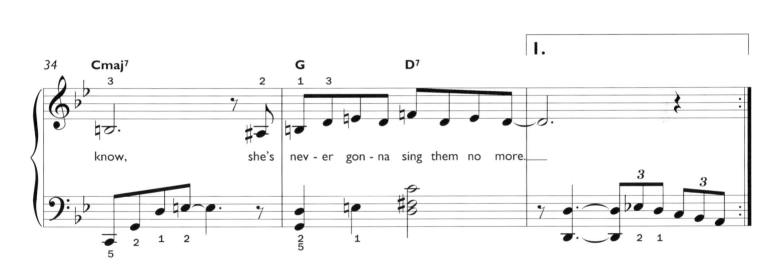

know, she's nev - er gon - na sing them no more.___

I.

2.

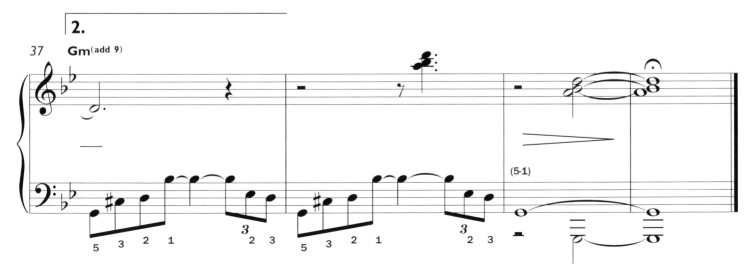

Please Send Me Someone To Love

Words & Music by Percy Mayfield

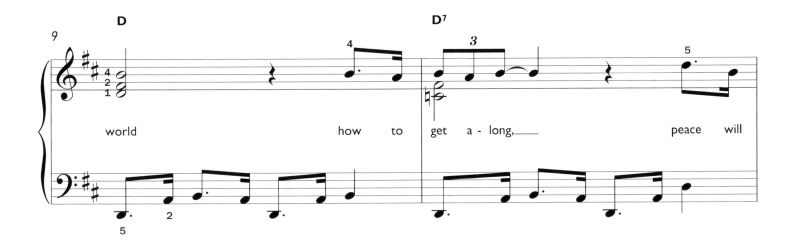

world ... how to get a - long,___ peace will

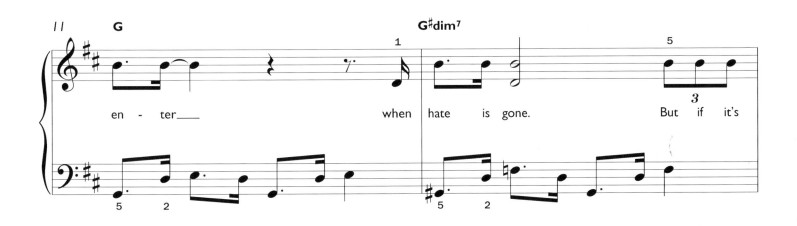

en - ter___ ... when hate is gone. But if it's

not ask - ing too much,___ please,_ send me some - one___ to

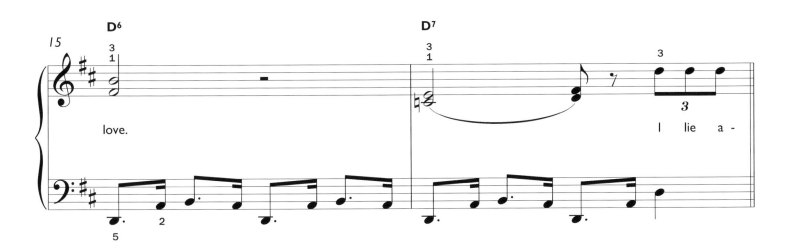

love. ... I lie a -

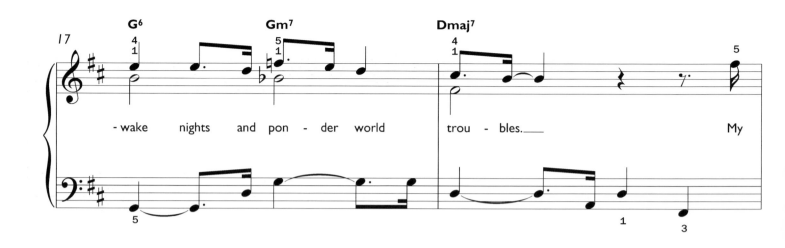

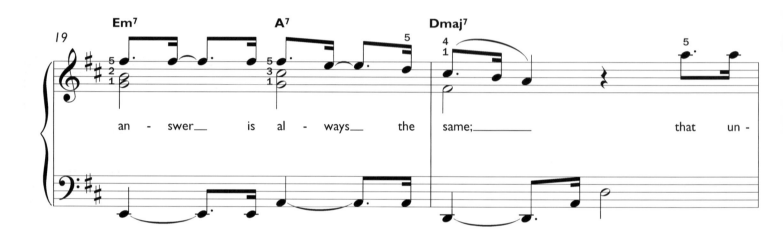

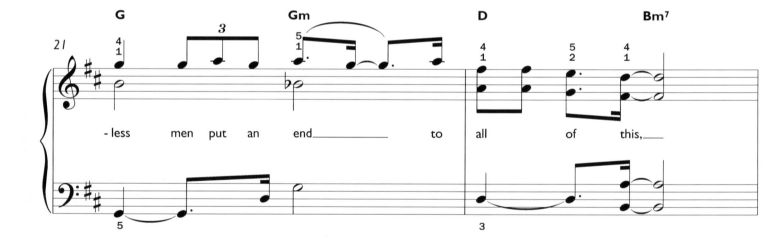

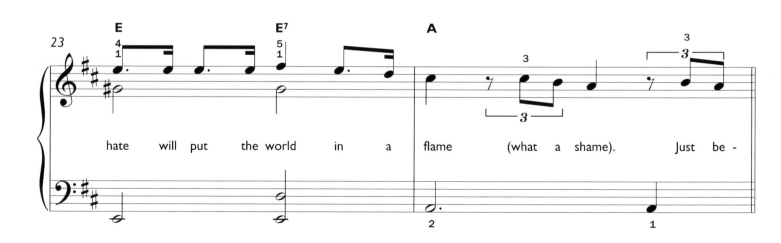

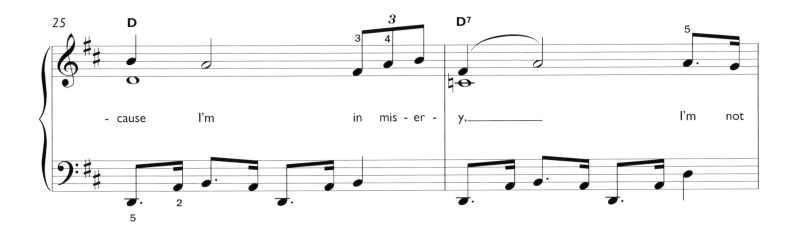

cause I'm   in mis - er - y,_____   I'm not

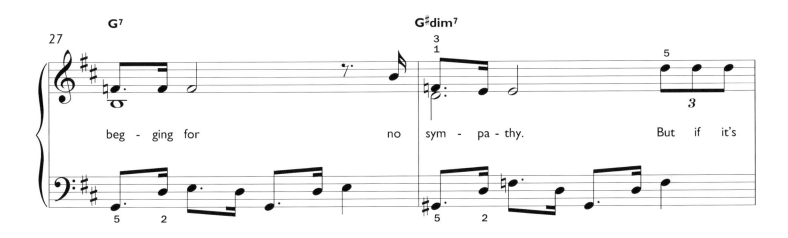

beg - ging for   no sym - pa - thy.   But if it's

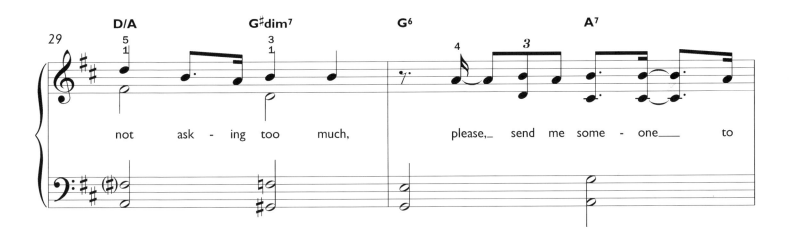

not ask - ing too much,   please,_ send me some - one____ to

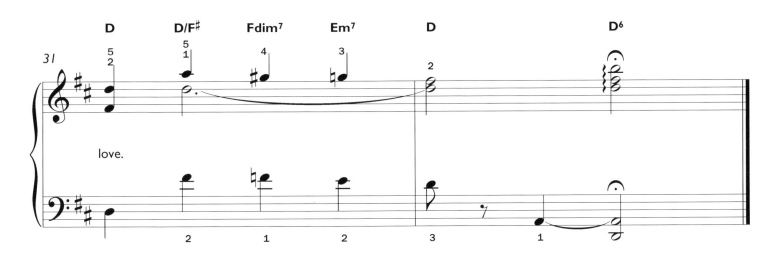

love.

Take The 'A' Train

Words & Music by Billy Strayhorn

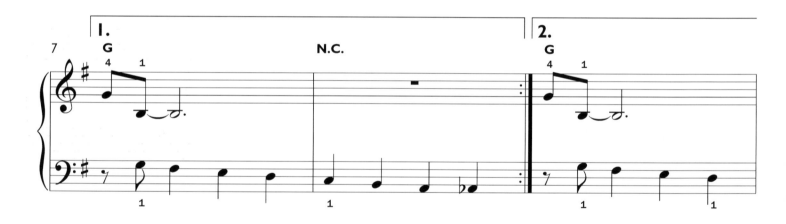

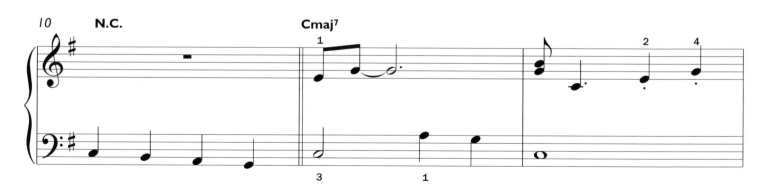

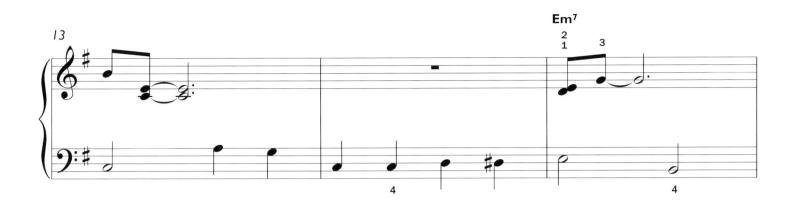

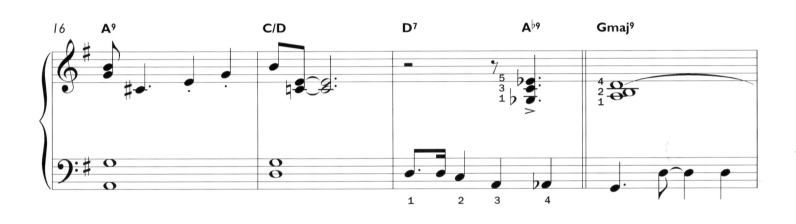

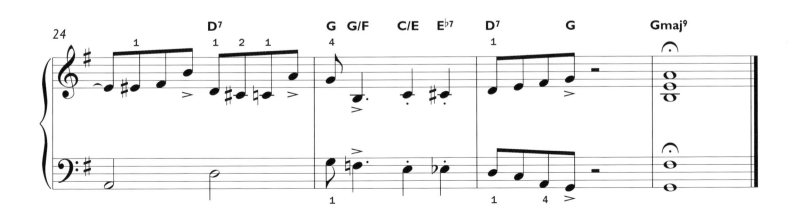

Bridge Over Troubled Water

Words & Music by Paul Simon

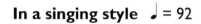

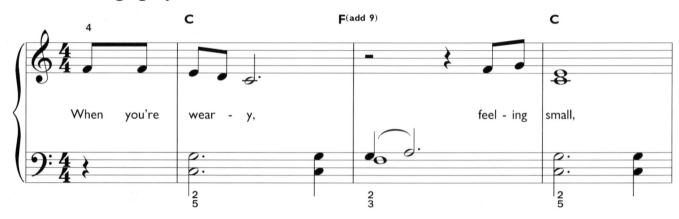

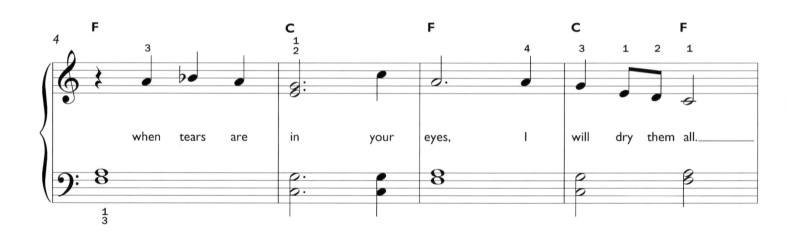

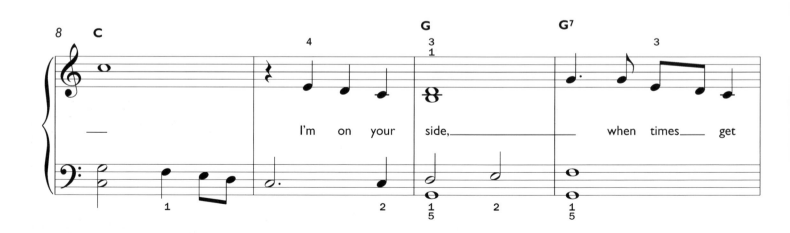

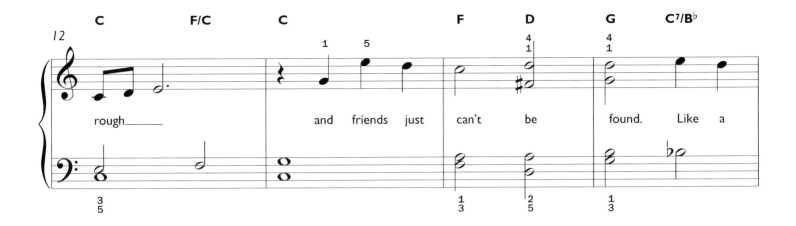

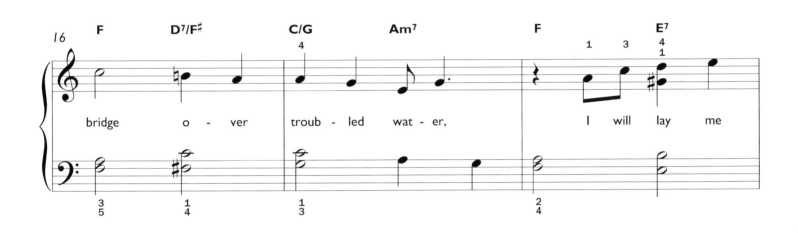

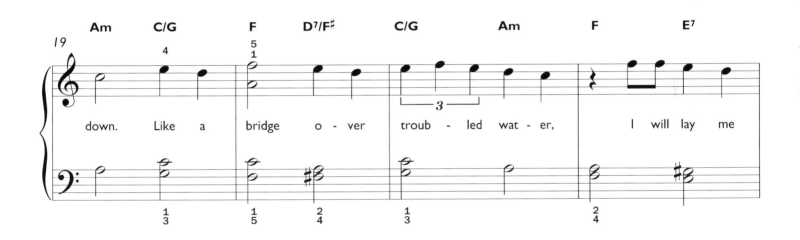

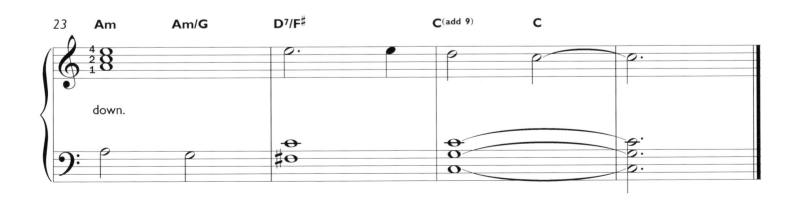

Dancing Queen

Words & Music by Benny Andersson, Stig Anderson & Björn Ulvaeus

Strong rock ♩ = 120

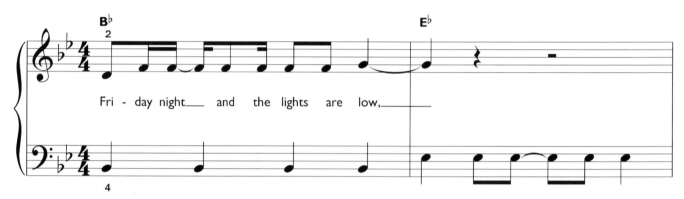

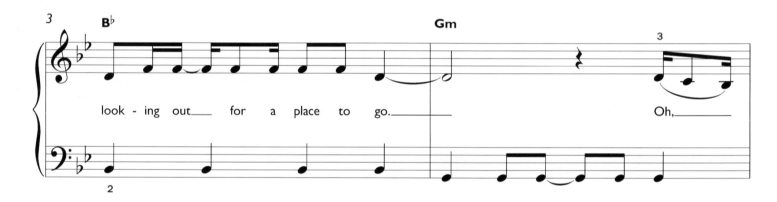

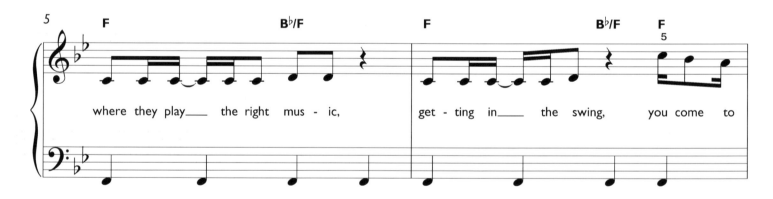

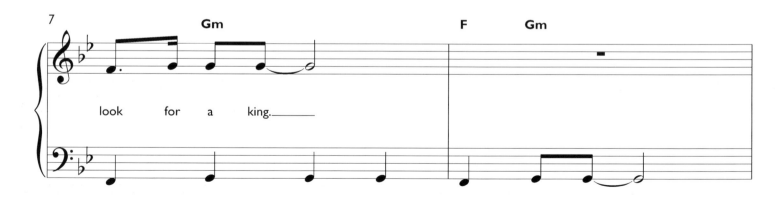

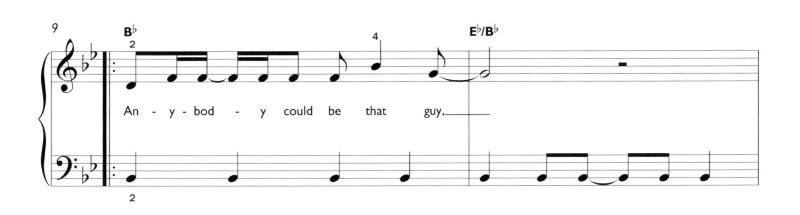

An - y - bod - y could be that guy,

night is young___ and the mus - ic's high;

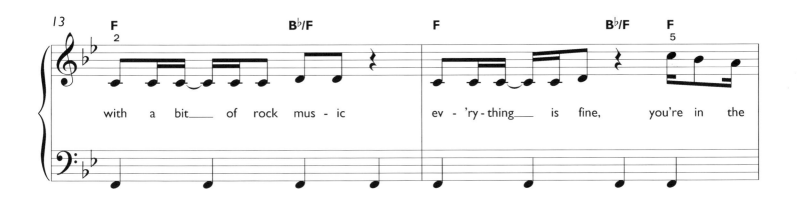

with a bit___ of rock mus - ic ev - 'ry - thing___ is fine, you're in the

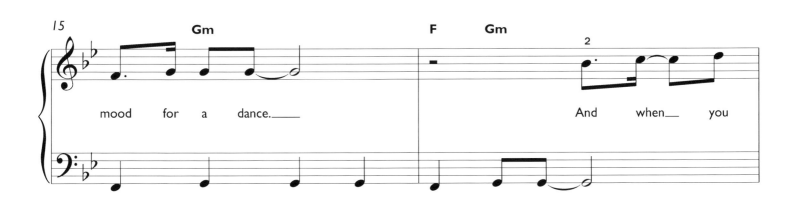

mood for a dance.___ And when___ you

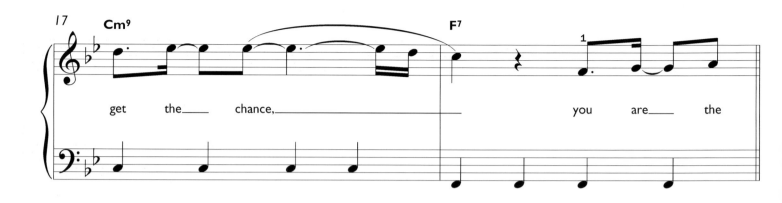

get the___ chance,_____ you are___ the

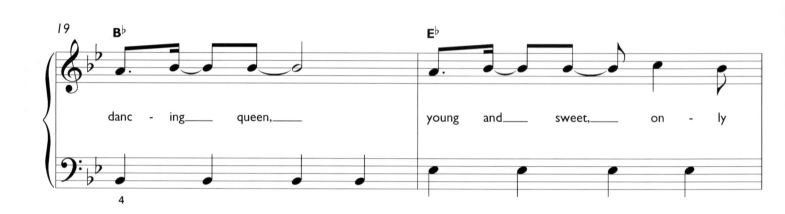

danc - ing___ queen,___ young and___ sweet,___ on - ly

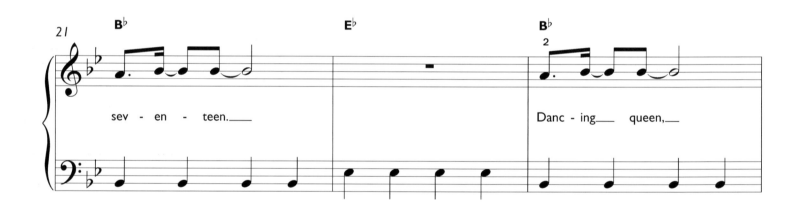

sev - en - teen.___ Danc - ing___ queen,___

feel the___ beat___ from the tam - bour - ine._____

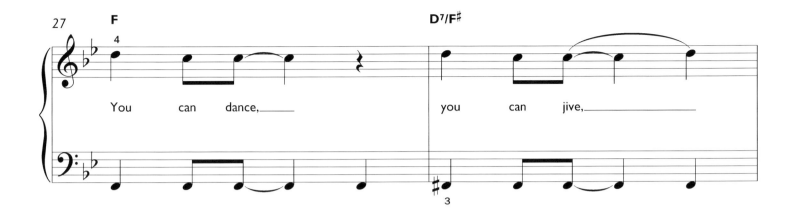

You can dance,____ you can jive,_____

hav - ing____ the time of____ your life;_____ oh,_____

see that____ girl,____ watch that____ scene,____ dig - gin' the

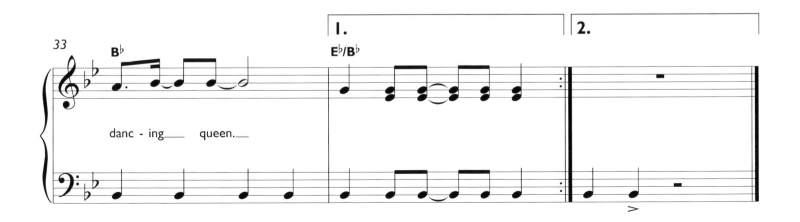

danc - ing____ queen.____

Let It Be

Words & Music by John Lennon & Paul McCartney

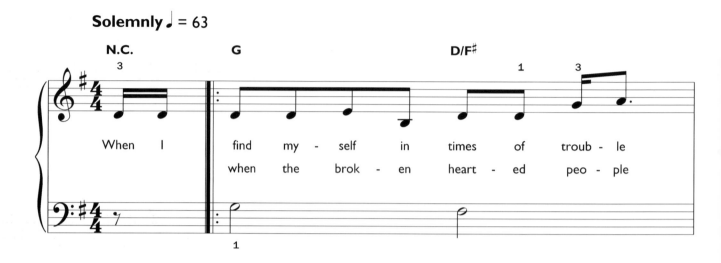

When I find my - self in times of troub - le
when the brok - en heart - ed peo - ple

Moth - er Mar - y comes to me, speak - ing words of wis - dom, let it
liv - ing in the world a - gree, there will be an an - swer, let it

be._____ And in my hour of dark - ness she is
be._____ For though they may be part - ed, there is

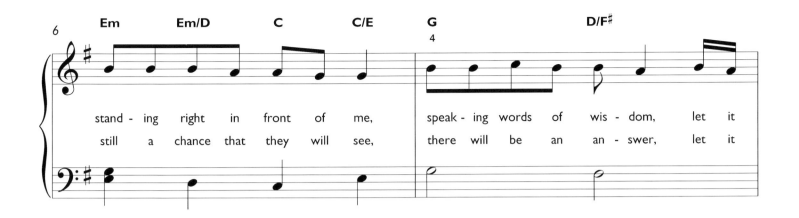

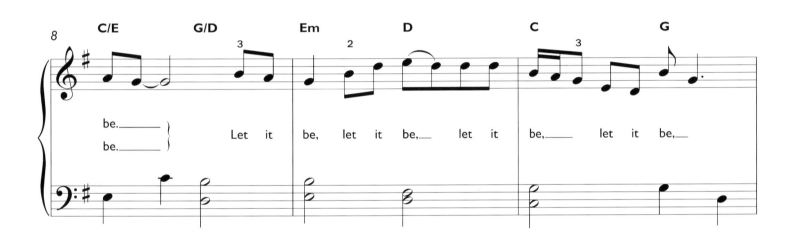

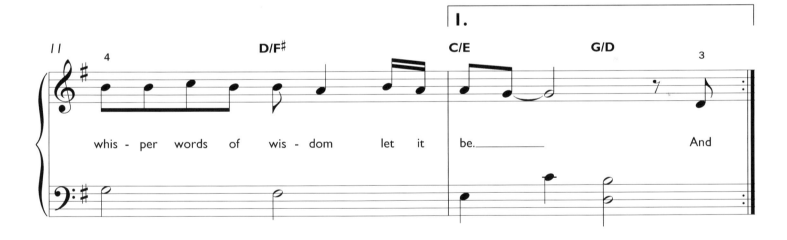

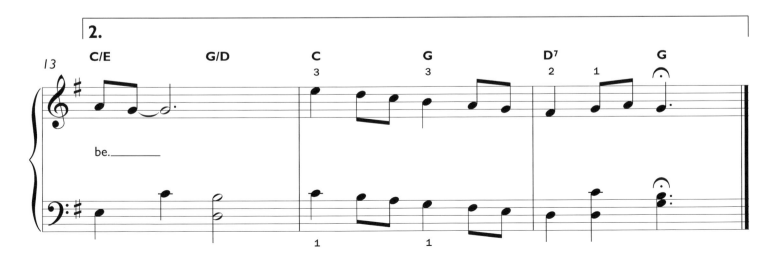

Somethin' Stupid

Words & Music by C. Carson Parks

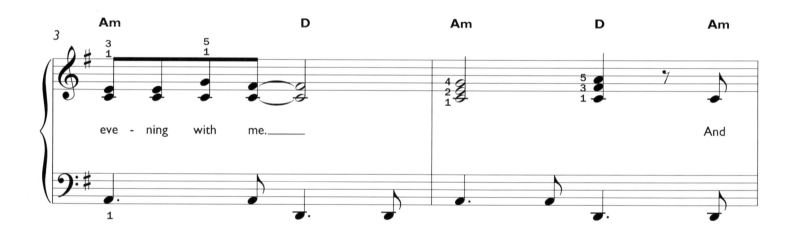

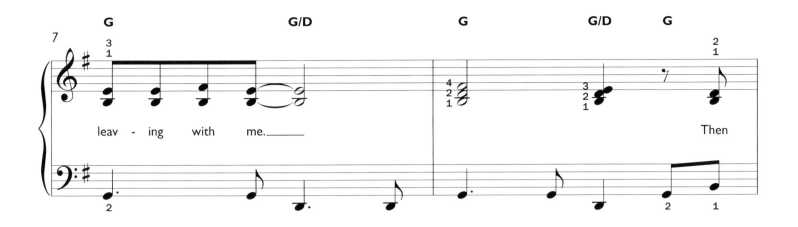

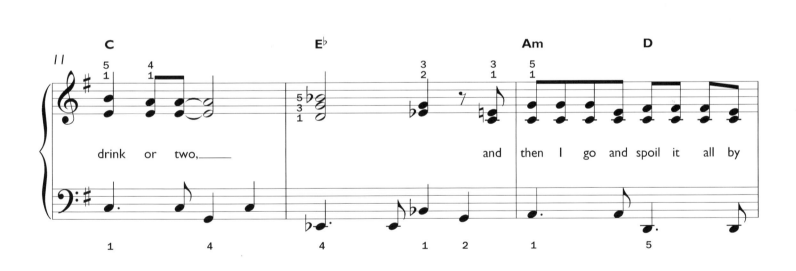

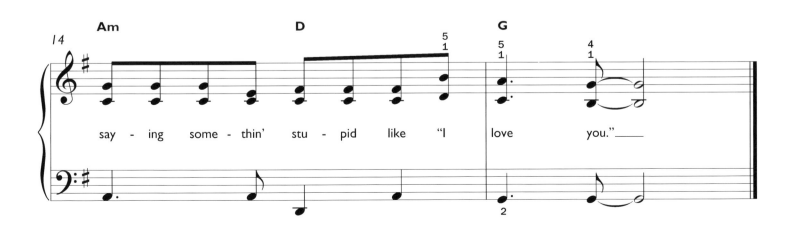

Your Song

Words & Music by Elton John & Bernie Taupin

Can't Help Lovin' Dat Man

(from 'Showboat')

Words by Oscar Hammerstein II, Music by Jerome Kern

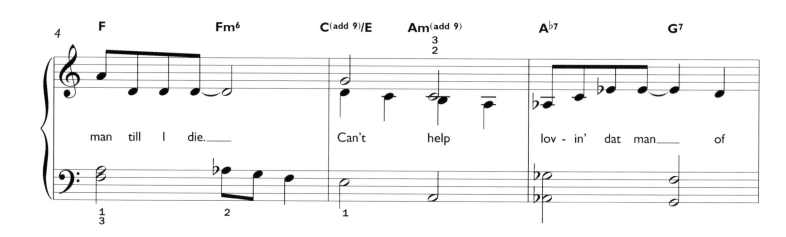

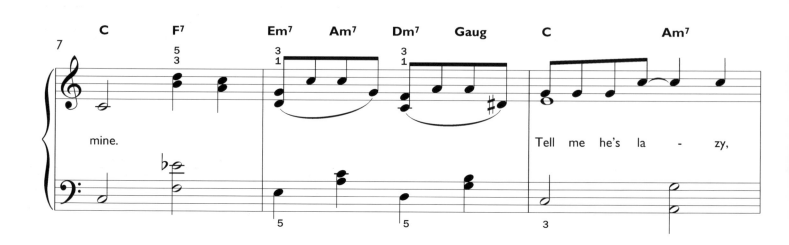

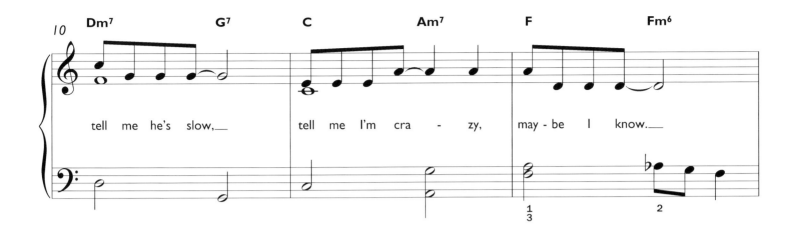

tell me he's slow,___ tell me I'm cra - zy, may - be I know.___

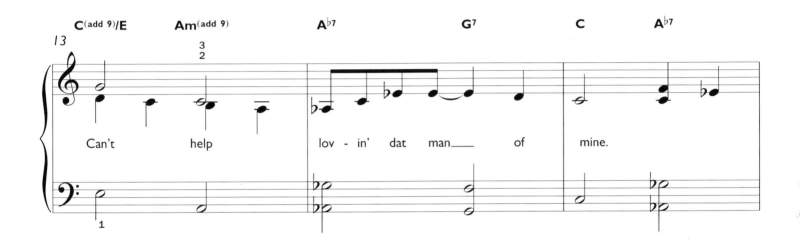

Can't help lov - in' dat man___ of mine.

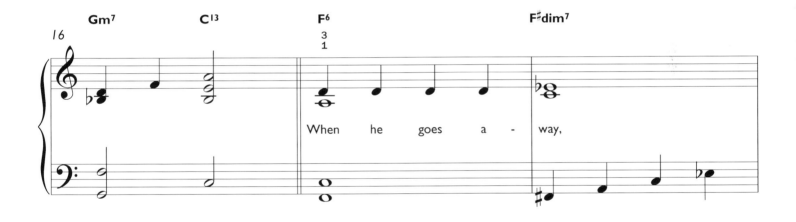

When he goes a - way,

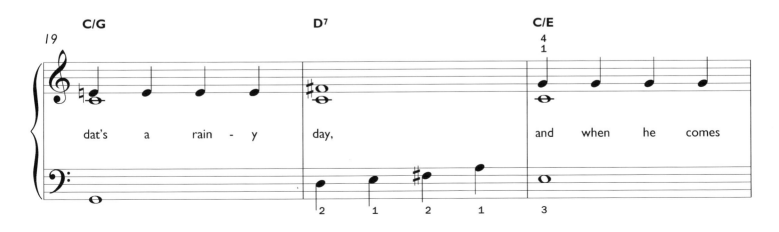

dat's a rain - y day, and when he comes

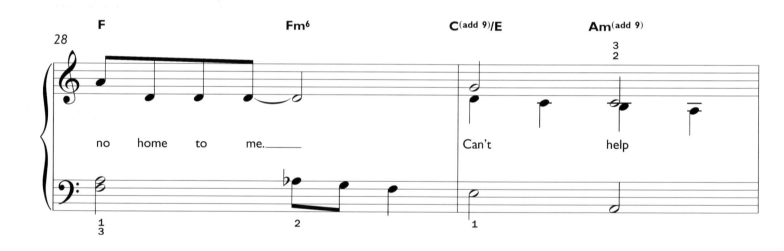

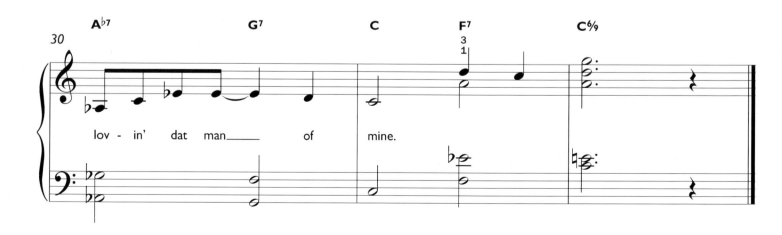

Close Every Door

(from 'Joseph And The Amazing Technicolor® Dreamcoat')

Music by Andrew Lloyd Webber, Lyrics by Tim Rice

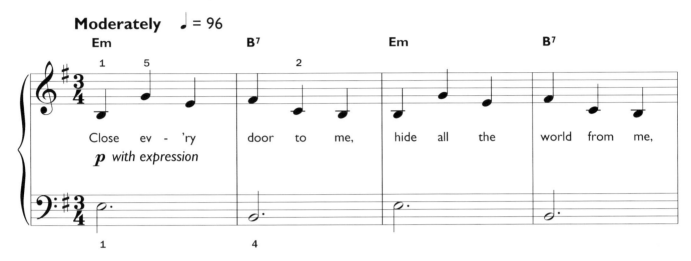

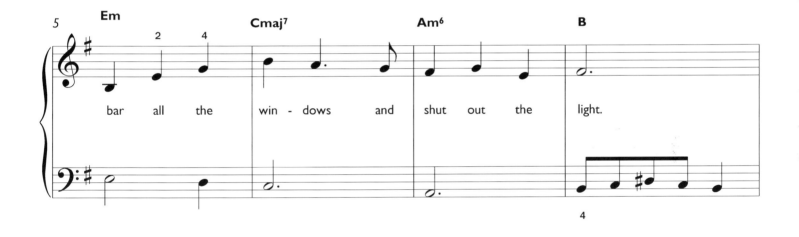

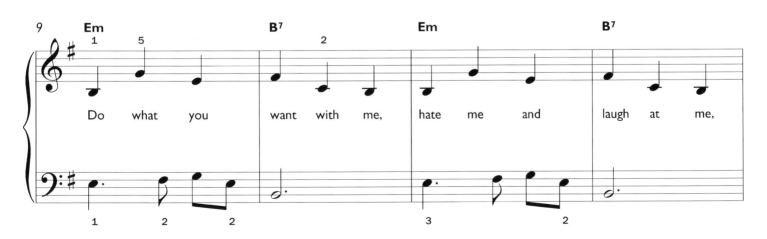

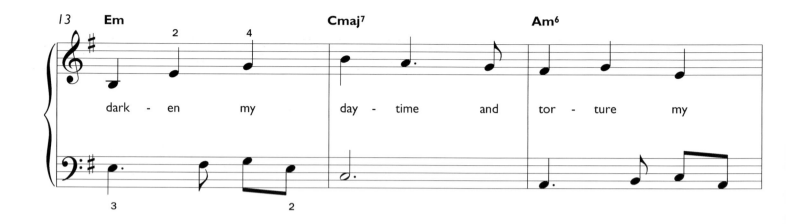

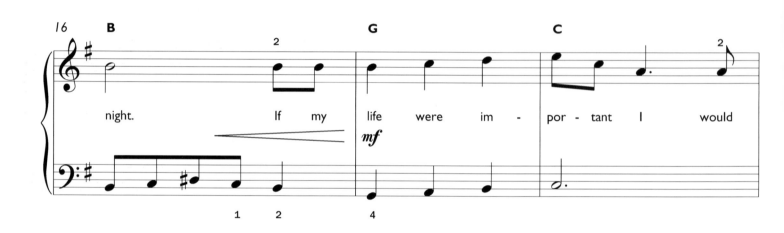

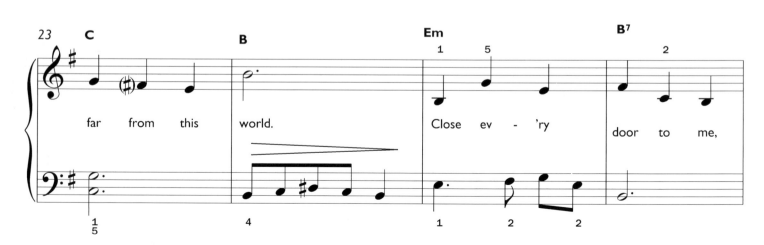

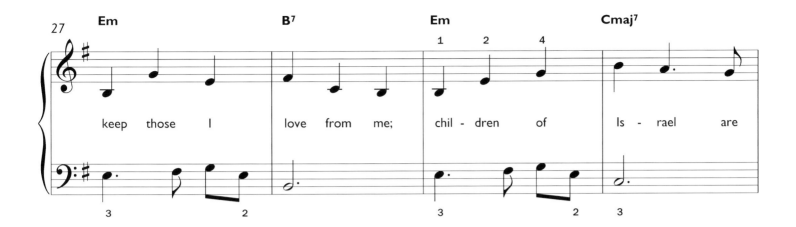

keep those I love from me; chil - dren of Is - rael are

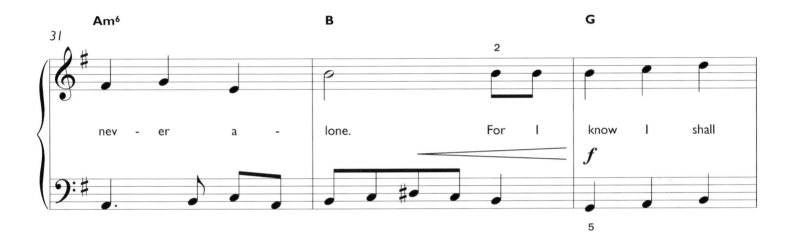

nev - er a - lone. For I know I shall

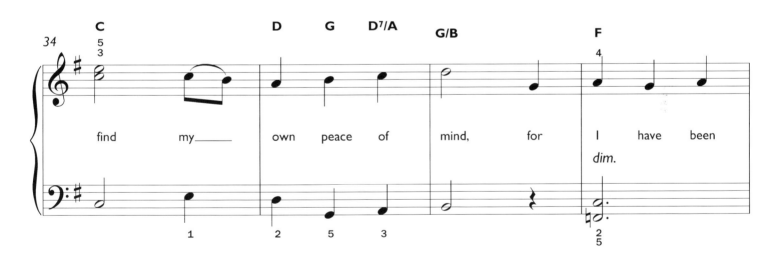

find my____ own peace of mind, for I have been

prom - ised a land____ of my own.

Maybe This Time

Words by Fred Ebb, Music by John Kander

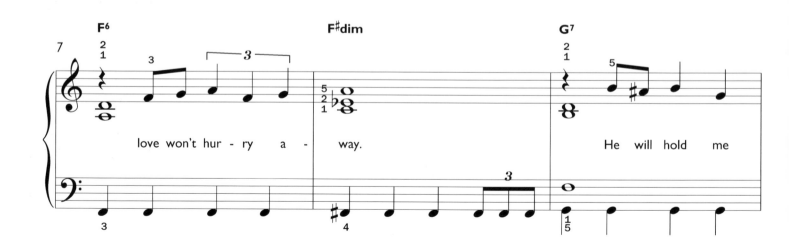

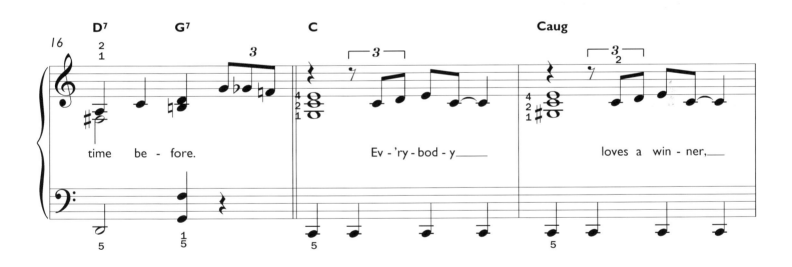

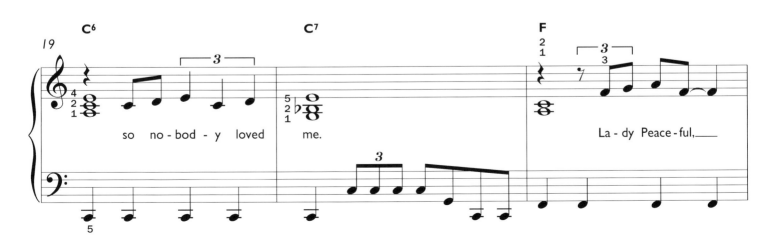

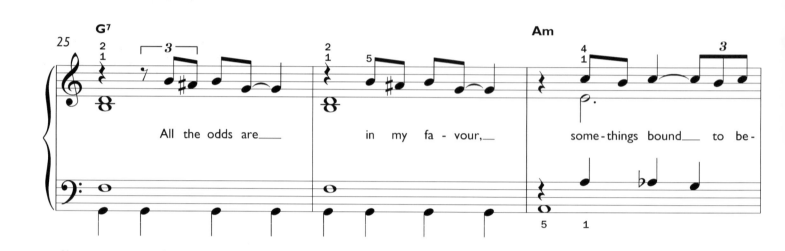

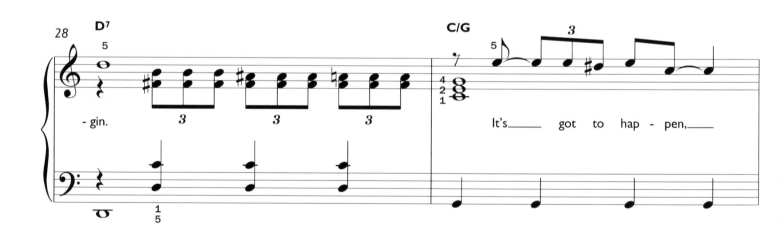

One

(from 'A Chorus Line')

Words by Edward Kleban, Music by Marvin Hamlisch

Fast and snappily ♩ = 116

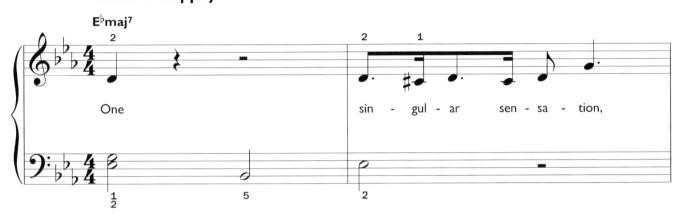

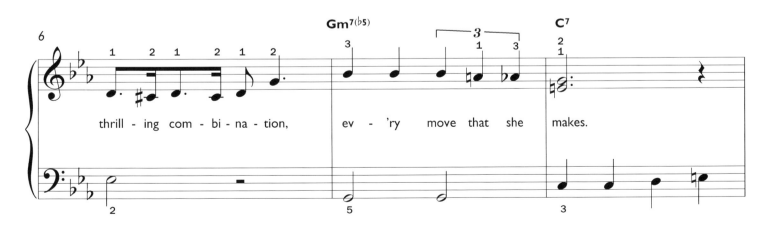

One smile and sud - den - ly no - bod - y else will

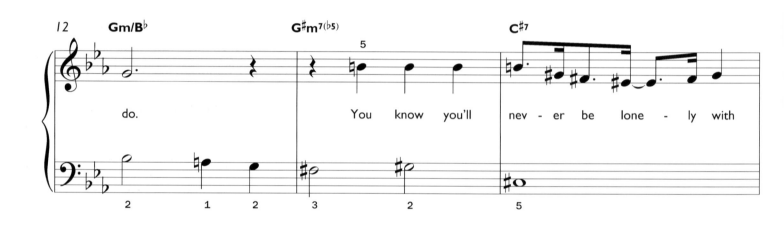

do. You know you'll nev - er be lone - ly with

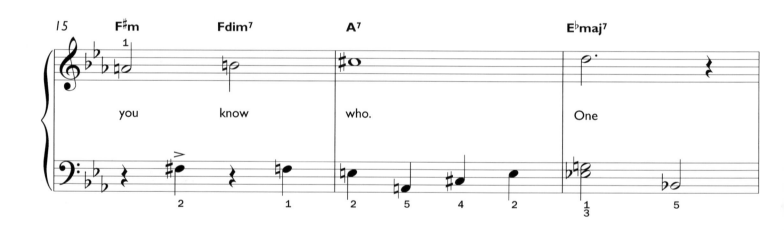

you know who. One

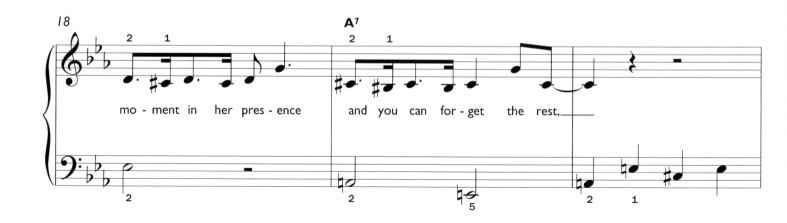

mo - ment in her pres - ence and you can for - get the rest,

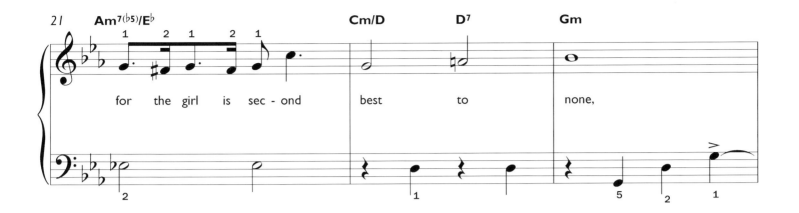

for the girl is sec - ond   best   to   none,

son.   Ooh!   Sigh!   Give her your   at - ten - tion.

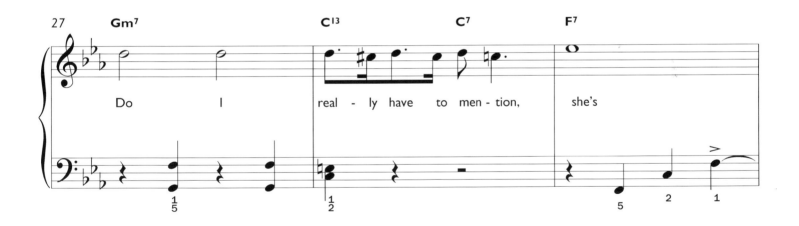

Do   I   real - ly have   to men - tion,   she's

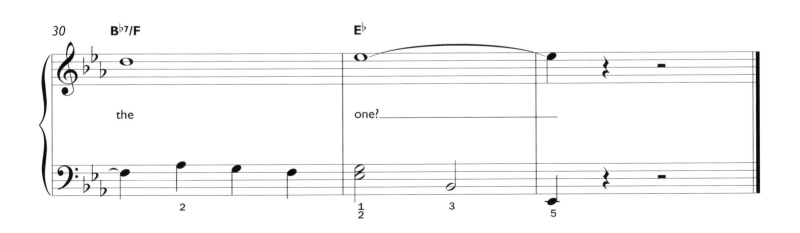

the   one?

Superstar

(from 'Jesus Christ Superstar')

Music by Andrew Lloyd Webber, Lyrics by Tim Rice

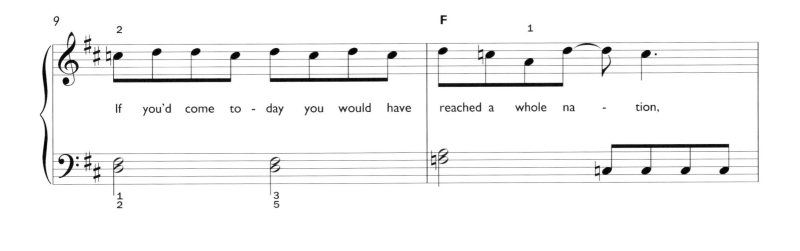

If you'd come to-day you would have reached a whole na - tion,

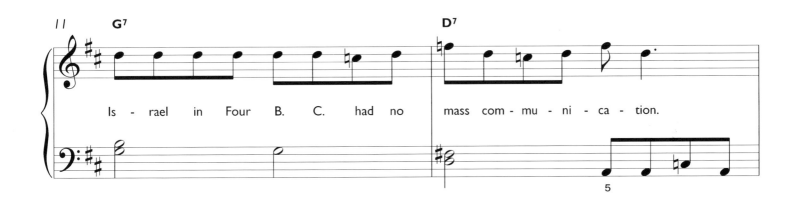

G7 Is - rael in Four B. C. had no **D7** mass com - mu - ni - ca - tion.

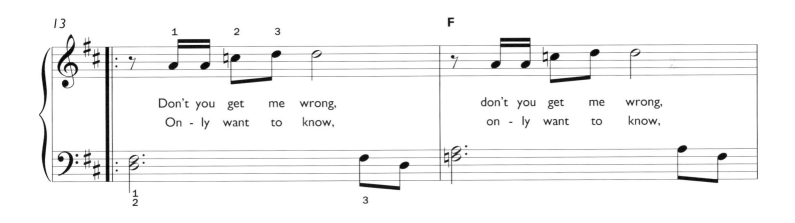

Don't you get me wrong,
On - ly want to know,

F don't you get me wrong,
on - ly want to know,

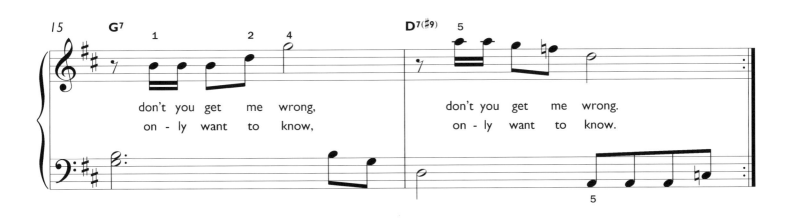

G7 don't you get me wrong,
on - ly want to know,

D7(♯9) don't you get me wrong.
on - ly want to know.

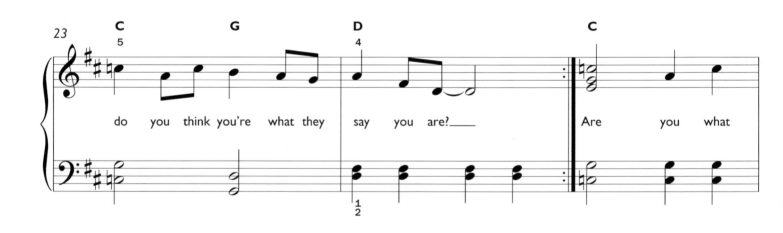

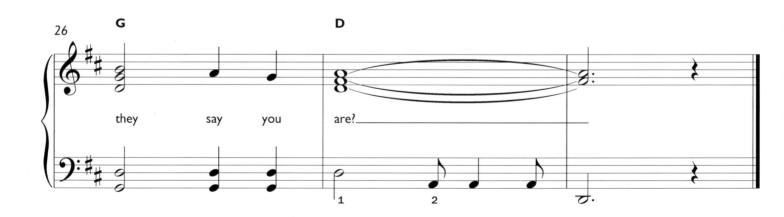